TRENDS IN GERONTOLOGY

TRENDS

IN **GERONTOLOGY**

SECOND EDITION

NATHAN W. SHOCK

Chief of the Gerontology Branch
of the National Heart Institute
and the Baltimore City Hospitals

STANFORD UNIVERSITY PRESS, Stanford, California, 1957

STANFORD UNIVERSITY PRESS, STANFORD, CALIFORNIA
LONDON: OXFORD UNIVERSITY PRESS
© 1957 by the Board of Trustees of the Leland Stanford Junior University
All Rights Reserved
Printed in the United States of America
Library of Congress Catalog Card Number: 57-12101

To Aunt Dilla

who learned the secret

of youth in old age

PREFACE

In the five years that have elapsed since publication of the first edition of *Trends in Gerontology,* interest in aging has expanded at a phenomenal rate. This rising interest has been accompanied by many new developments, both in research and in action programs. In order to characterize these new developments, it was necessary to rewrite, rather than revise, *Trends in Gerontology.*

This volume surveys the current status of activities in the field of aging and attempts to assess current trends in terms of major developments since 1950. The book is written for the informed lay reader rather than the specialist. It attempts to bring together the many facets of gerontology and to provide key references with illustrative data. In a field that is expanding as rapidly as gerontology, any statement of current status is bound to be outmoded even before it appears in print. We therefore offer apologies for omissions, some of which have been made necessary by space limitations. Among the many new developments, particularly in action programs, it has been necessary to describe only examples rather than to strive for completeness.

Bibliographic citations have been kept to a minimum, since all references to the literature may be found in *A Classified Bibliography of Gerontology and Geriatrics* (1951; *Supplement,* 1957).

Thanks are due Richard I. Myers and Michael Potash for assistance in assembling and abstracting the many research articles that were consulted. The assistance of Marianne Rabette in typing and preparing the manuscript for publication is gratefully acknowledged. Without the aid of many agencies and individuals, who furnished information about their activities and programs, it would have been impossible to complete the manuscript.

Because of its desire to contribute to improvements in the care of the aged, the Forest Park Foundation of Peoria, Illinois, created in 1939 by Mr. W. H. Sommers, Dr. Leslie Rutherford, and Mr. Howard Kinsey, has encouraged the completion of this volume and has made a financial contribution toward its publication. This support is gratefully acknowledged.

All of the opinions expressed are those of the author and are not necessarily those of the Department of Health, Education and Welfare, the Public Health Service, or any other organization.

NATHAN W. SHOCK

Baltimore, Maryland
September 1, 1957

CONTENTS

1

INTRODUCTION

Gerontology is the scientific study of the phenomena of aging. By aging, we mean the progressive changes which take place in a cell, a tissue, an organ system, a total organism, or a group of organisms with the passage of time. All living things change with time in both structure and function, and the changes which follow a general trend constitute aging. Although aging begins with conception and ends only with death, gerontology is concerned primarily with the changes which occur between the attainment of maturity and death of the individual, and the factors that influence these progressive changes. These factors may range from the influences of heredity to differences in climatic factors, and include the effects of social customs and usages. Gerontology is concerned not only with changes in structure and function in individuals with the passage of time, but also with their reactions to one another, and to their environment.

The problems of gerontology fall into four major categories: (1) social and economic problems precipitated by an increasing number of elderly people in the population, (2) psychological aspects of aging within individuals, and their reactions to one another, (3) physiological bases of aging, along with pathological deviations and disease processes, and (4) general biological aspects of aging in all animal species. As aging individuals, each of us has a direct interest in the practical problems of a social and economic nature. Solutions for these problems rest on knowledge of the psychological and physiological changes that occur with increasing age, as well as on knowledge about the prevention, cure, and amelioration of diseases. A complete understanding of the age changes in physiological and psychological functions depends, in turn, on a more detailed knowledge of the way that cells and tissues function; i.e., basic studies on biology, biochemistry, and physiology of cells and tissues. Thus, the solution of practical problems is dependent upon an extension of our knowledge in a wide variety of scientific disciplines.

It is obvious that most of the practical problems of gerontology contain elements from a number of these categories. Thus, providing adequate care for elderly people involves questions of economics, community organization, services to older people, the incidence of diseases and their prevention, the personal characteristics of the aging individual and his relationships with others in the community. However, we can identify a whole array of problems within each of the categories listed.

Social and economic problems.—We know that the age structure of our population has changed significantly since 1900, but we need to establish valid projections for the future. Income maintenance for aging people involves not only questions of national income and the level of payments aging people need and what our economy will support, but also questions of continued employment for the aging. Recommendations for the employment of the elderly depend upon knowledge of motivation, learning capacity, retraining, and rehabilitation; questions which extend into the psychological area with roots in physiology. Recommendations for adequate housing and care of older people depend on information about the relative effectiveness of institutional care, private homes for the aged, construction and operation of communities for retired individuals, and the role of public housing for older people. The organization and coordination of community resources for providing the services needed by older people, and the more important question of how the competence and skills of older people can be utilized to the best advantage for the entire community, represent another important research area. Health maintenance and medical care not only require knowledge about the social and economic aspects of aging, but are dependent on more detailed knowledge about the incidence and prevention of disease. It is here that important medical research into the causes, prevention, and treatment of diseases such as cardiovascular ailments, mental disease, cancer, arthritis, etc., extends even further into aspects of cellular function, biochemistry, biophysics, and other basic sciences.

Psychological aspects.—Psychological problems involve questions about age changes in personality structure, intellectual capacities, perceptual functions, and emotional characteristics. Many of these, such as perceptual functions and emotional characteristics, depend in part upon physiological research. Age changes in intellectual function include learning capacities, motivation, and the effects of cultural patterns on motivation and behavior. Knowledge about the basic psychological needs of older people has an important bearing on planning community programs.

Physiology of aging and disease processes.—Physiology is concerned with the quantitative description not only of changes in the performance of various organ systems, but also of the effectiveness with which these systems work together to maintain health and vigor in the individual. Complete understanding of these processes obviously depends on investigations of structure and function of individual cells and tissues. Similarly, the effects of various diseases on performance fall in this category. Geriatrics is a term used to describe the branch of medical science that is concerned with the medical and pathological problems of older people. It includes methods for maintaining health and vitality, as well as the treatment of disease states in older people, and is thus a part of the broader field of gerontology.

Biological aspects of aging.—The biology of aging includes studies on cells and tissues from all species of animals and plants. By using lower animal species for study, we can maintain genetic and environmental controls and can hope to isolate the factors that influence longevity and determine the probability of death. Within biology we can identify studies on genetic factors, structural and functional characteristics of cells and tissues, and the basic mechanisms of cellular physiology. Although much remains to be learned, we now know that because of the diversity of rates of aging among different individuals, as well as between different organ systems within the same individual, no specific answer can be given to the question "When does old age begin?" Aging is a dynamic equilibrium. The individual animal, at any age, is the result of processes of accumulation and degradation that take place simultaneously. In youth, equilibrium is shifted in favor of accumulation. The rate of building up is more rapid than the rate of tearing down. The rate of change is greatest in the fetus, less in the infant, still less in the child, and after maturity is usually so slow that it can be measured only by widely spaced observations.

The goals of gerontology.—The ultimate goal of action programs in the field of aging is to minimize the individual and social handicaps of old age as they now exist. This means giving every individual the maximum opportunity for healthy old age with meaning to himself and his community. These practical issues have their bases in fundamental questions about the process of aging as a biological phenomenon, as well as about the psychological and physiological characteristics of aging people. Experience has shown that our ability to devise adequate action programs depends on a firm knowledge of the processes involved. The support of basic research in all aspects of aging is therefore essential. The goal of research in gerontology is not to extend the life span, but to minimize disabilities and handicaps of old age. Attainment of this goal will require the considered efforts of scientists trained in all disciplines, working individually and collaboratively, as well as the careful thought of individuals who are competent to synthesize and correlate information from many fields.

2

TRENDS IN | **POPULATION**

Although the total population of the United
States continues to increase, the rate of growth of the age group 65
and over is rising at an even greater rate. Between 1900 and 1950,
the total population of the United States doubled, but the number of
persons aged 65 years and over quadrupled. In 1900, only 4 in every
100 Americans were over age 65, whereas today the proportion is
over 8 in every 100. According to the 1950 census, there were
12,271,000 people over age 65 out of the total population of 150,697,000.
Table 1 shows estimates for total population and the number over
age 65 for five-year periods up to 1975, at which time it is estimated
there will be over 20.7 million over the age of 65. If these estimates
are in error, they are in all probability low, since past experience has
shown that predictions of future population are usually underesti-
mated rather than overestimated. Thus, the prediction of 1950 population, made in 1947, gave a total of 146,087,000, with 7.7 percent
over age 65. The actual count in 1950 was 150,697,000, with 8.1 percent over age 65.

World-wide changes in population structure.—Shifts in the proportion of older people in the population are taking place throughout
the world. In 1953, 11.5 percent of the population of France was 65
years of age and over (Figure 1). In contrast, Mexico and India
showed only approximately 3.5 percent of their total population as
over the age of 65. Thus, the cultural pattern, economic level, public
health status, and, perhaps most significantly, infantile death rate,
coupled with birth rate, play a major role in determining the proportion of older people in a population.

Regional distribution.—Even within the United States, there are
regional differences in the distribution of older people. In 1950, the
number of persons 65 years of age and over ranged from 5 per 100

TABLE 1

TOTAL POPULATION, AND POPULATION 65 YEARS AND OVER:
UNITED STATES, SPECIFIED YEARS*

Year	Total Population		Population 65 and Over		Population 65 and Over as Percent of Total
	Number	1900 = 100	Number	1900 = 100	
1900......	75,994,575	100	3,080,498	100	4.1
1910......	91,972,266	121	3,949,524	128	4.3
1920......	105,710,620	139	4,933,215	160	4.7
1930......	122,775,046	161	6,633,805	215	5.4
1940......	131,669,275	173	9,019,314	292	6.8
1950......	150,697,361	198	12,271,178	398	8.1
Estimates					
1955......	164,782,000	217	13,973,000	454	8.5
1960......	177,426,000	233	15,701,000	511	8.9
1965......	189,916,000	250	17,336,000	563	9.1
1970......	204,222,000	269	18,885,000	613	9.3
1975......	220,982,000	290	20,689,000	671	9.4

* Sources: Bureau of the Census, *Sixteenth Census of the United States, Population,* Vol. II, Part 1, Table 8; *U.S. Census of Population, 1950, Vol. II, Characteristics of the Population,* Part 1, United States Summary, Table 39; *Current Population Reports, Population Estimates,* Series P-25, No. 39, Table 1, and No. 78, Aug. 21, 1953, Series A.

in New Mexico to 11 per 100 in New Hampshire.[1] The maximum concentration of older people was in the New England States and the Great Plains States (over 9 percent of the population of the state). The lowest percentages were found in the South and Southwest (under 7 percent). The low proportions of aged people in the South Atlantic and Southwestern States is partly the result of high birth rates.

Migration of the elderly.—Although it is extremely difficult to specify precisely the effects of migration, it is possible to tabulate the areas of greatest increase in the proportion of the population 65 and over in the United States. Between 1940 and 1950, the greatest change in the proportion of persons over age 65 occurred in Arizona, California, Florida, and Nevada. These states also gained substantially

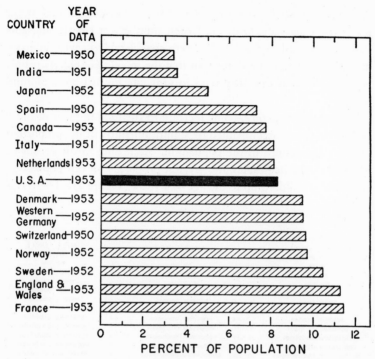

FIG. 1—Percentage of population aged 65 and over in selected countries of the world. Data from *Demographic Yearbook, 1954*, 6th ed., Statistical Office of the United Nations, 1954.

in total population, but the percentage of people over age 65 still increased.[2] More detailed analyses of migration among the aged have shown that, between 1940 and 1950, Florida gained over 40 percent of its increment in people over the age of 65 by migration alone, as compared with approximately 17 percent in California, even though the absolute numbers of migrants was greater in California (130,000) than in Florida (approximately 66,400).[3,4] In both states, the migration in 1940–50 was almost double that of 1930–40 among the aged. In contrast, New York, Pennsylvania, and Illinois lost population over age 65 by out-migration. However, on a percentage basis, North Dakota, South Dakota, Vermont, Wyoming, and Montana showed the greatest losses (13 percent). It was also found that the percentage losses from the states with the largest numbers of elderly migrants (New York and Pennsylvania) were considerably heavier in 1940–50 than in 1930–40. Thus, it seems that the mobility of elderly people is increasing and that they tend to gravitate toward areas of mild climate.

Population structure.—The increase in the total number of older persons has been accompanied by significant shifts in the proportion of other age groups in the population. According to the census of 1900 for the United States, the greatest proportion of our population consisted of children up to the age of 4 years (Figure 2). There was

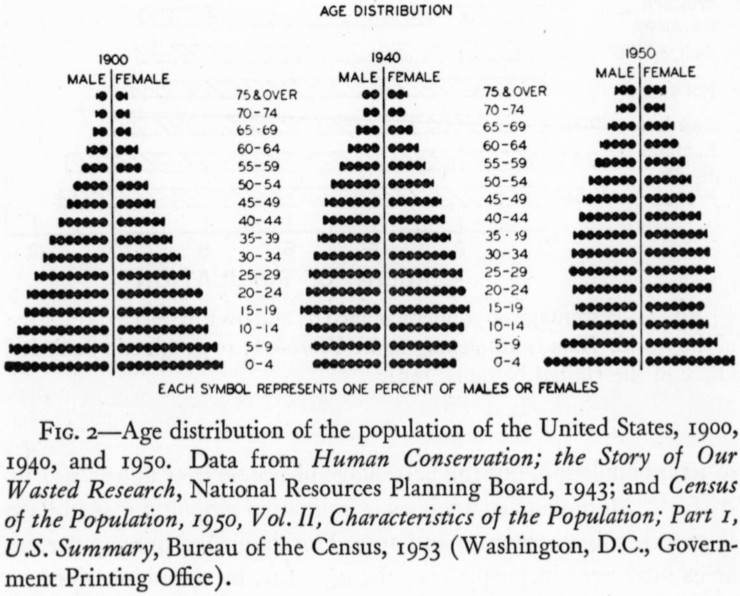

AGE DISTRIBUTION

	1900				1940				1950	
	MALE	FEMALE			MALE	FEMALE			MALE	FEMALE
			75 & OVER				75 & OVER			
			70–74				70–74			
			65–69				65–69			
			60–64				60–64			
			55–59				55–59			
			50–54				50–54			
			45–49				45–49			
			40–44				40–44			
			35–39				35–39			
			30–34				30–34			
			25–29				25–29			
			20–24				20–24			
			15–19				15–19			
			10–14				10–14			
			5–9				5–9			
			0–4				0–4			

EACH SYMBOL REPRESENTS ONE PERCENT OF MALES OR FEMALES

FIG. 2—Age distribution of the population of the United States, 1900, 1940, and 1950. Data from *Human Conservation; the Story of Our Wasted Research*, National Resources Planning Board, 1943; and *Census of the Population, 1950, Vol. II, Characteristics of the Population; Part 1, U.S. Summary*, Bureau of the Census, 1953 (Washington, D.C., Government Printing Office).

a gradual reduction in the proportion of the population at increasing ages, so that at the age of 75 and above only slightly over 1 percent of the population fell in this age category. In 1940, the number of young children diminished significantly; the 15–19 age group was the most numerous. By 1950, the scarce crop of 1940 babies resulted in a marked reduction in the 10–14 age group, but the increased birth rate of the war years had again broadened the base of the population pyramid. Examination of Figure 2 shows that there has been a gradual increment in the proportion of the population that is extending upward, so that by 1950 over 2.5 percent of the population was 75 years of age and over. Contrary to expectations, the birth rate since 1950 has remained relatively high, so that the group of wage earners 20 to 65 will have not only increasing numbers of elderly but also children of school age dependent upon them for support over the next 15 years. By this time, the children from the first wave of the increased births will have attained working age and will contribute to the total productivity of the nation. Thus, the composition of the population at any moment is a resultant of the interplay of many forces of which mortality rate and birth rate play major roles.

Average age of death.—The average age of death has been increasing steadily in the United States from 35 years in 1879 to 67.5 years in 1955 for white males (Figure 3). Within the next 10 years, it will probably be over 75 years for males and 80 years for females. Figure 3 also illustrates the greater longevity of females as compared with males. Before assuming that this difference in longevity between the sexes is a result of the greater pressures placed upon the male, it should be pointed out that similar sex differences were found in many species other than man, as, for instance, the rat, mouse, guinea pig, and even some insect forms.[5] One important social result of this difference between the sexes is that with increasing age there is a greater and greater proportion of females in the population. At birth, there are approximately 104 males per 100 females. However, at age 65 and over, there were in 1950 only 89.6 men per 100 women.[6] In the age group 65–74, approximately 18 percent of the males were widowed as compared with 47 percent of the females. At ages 75 and over, 38 percent of males were widowed as compared with 72 percent of females.[7] These facts have important implications for housing, community programs, and retirement plans. Figure 3 also indicates that improvements in hygiene, in economic status, and in living conditions that have resulted in the gradual increase in length of life since 1900 have had a greater effect among women than among men.

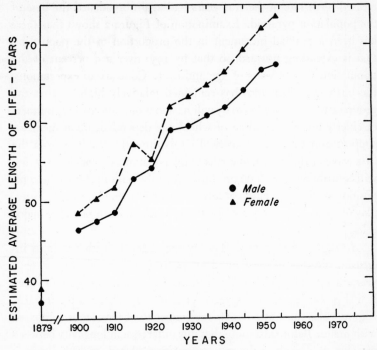

Fig. 3—Average age of death of white males and females in the United States, 1879–1954. Data from *Abridged Life Tables; United States, 1954,* Vital Statistics, Special Reports, National Summaries, **44**: No. 2 (May 15, 1956).

Thus, in 1900, the difference in life expectancy of white males and females was only approximately 2 years, whereas, in 1955, the difference between the sexes was 6.2 years. The full impact of this increased life expectancy on the world today can only be appreciated when viewed in historical perspective. Figure 4 shows a plot of our best estimates of average age of death from Greek and Roman times to the present. This graph shows the striking increment which has occurred almost within the last half-century. The presence of large numbers of older people in our society is thus without precedent and the number will apparently continue to rise for some years to come.

A good part of the increase in average length of life, illustrated

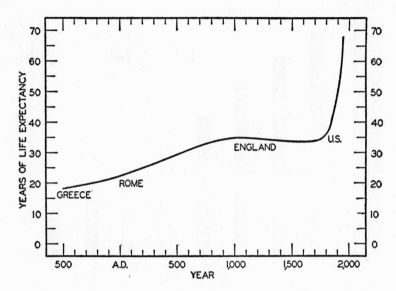

FIG. 4—Life expectancy from early times to the present, A.D. 500–1950 (estimated average age at death). Data from L. I. Dublin, A. J. Lotka, and M. Spiegelman, *Length of Life* (rev. ed., New York, Ronald Press, 1949), p. 42.

in Figure 3, is the result of saving lives at early ages through our success in reducing infant mortality and combating infectious diseases. The gradual improvement in living conditions and our knowledge of public health have also made important contributions. Figure 5 shows that the greatest increases in life expectancy between 1850 and 1950 appear at early ages. Thus, in 1850, the person who had survived the rigors of the diseases of infancy and escaped the infectious diseases of childhood and the fatal diseases of middle age, so that he attained the age of 60, had a 50–50 chance of living an additional 16 years. In 1950, the person who attained the age of 60 had an expectancy of approximately 18 years; an increase of only 2 years as compared with an increase of 57 years at birth since 1850. Although death rates for diseases such as diabetes, cancer, heart disease, and kidney disease have been increasing over the past 5 to 10 years, this does not necessarily reflect an increase in susceptibility to these diseases. It

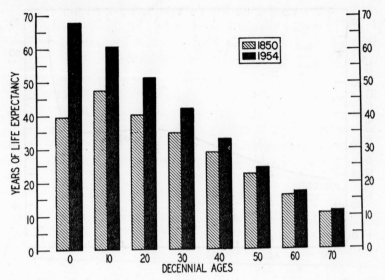

FIG. 5—Years of life expectancy remaining at each decade of life, for white males in the United States in 1850 and 1954. Data from L. I. Dublin, A. J. Lotka, and M. Spiegelman, *Length of Life* (rev. ed., New York, Ronald Press, 1949), p. 50; and *Abridged Life Tables; United States, 1954*, Vital Statistics, Special Reports, National Summaries, **44**: No. 2 (May 15, 1956).

may be explained simply on the basis that many individuals, who in earlier years would have succumbed to childhood diseases, are now living long enough to develop those diseases which appear only during middle age and later. Advances in medical research focused on heart disease and cancer, which are now the primary causes of death among older people, may result in striking increases in life expectancy of people in the older age groups. Thus, before the discovery and use of insulin in 1922, the average life expectancy of the 30-year-old diabetic was only 4 to 6 years. With the discovery of insulin and improvements in treatment, life expectancy of the 30-year-old diabetic has increased from an additional 16.8 years in 1922–25 to 30.5 years in 1939–45, and to almost 35 years in 1955.

The effects of new discoveries and changes in methods of treatment of specific disease on life expectancy are further illustrated in Figure 6. Death rates from pneumonia and influenza among the group 65 years of age and over have changed remarkably between 1900 and 1955. The arrows indicate the approximate time of introduction of new therapeutic agents. From death rates of 700–1,000 per 100,000 population in 1900–1915, the introduction of serum treatments in 1930 was followed by a drop in deaths to around 500 per 100,000 population. In 1939–40, the introduction of the sulfa drugs produced a further drop, and with the use of penicillin, beginning about 1947–48, the death rate among this older age group has fallen

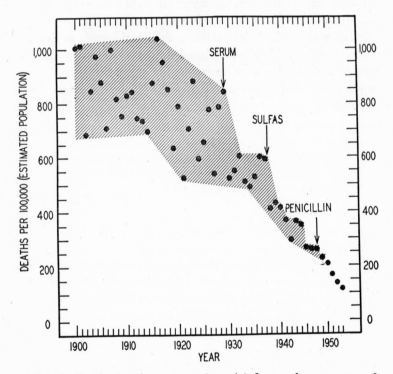

Fig. 6—Death rates for pneumonia and influenza for age group 65 years and over; death registration states, 1900–1955 (ratio per 100,000 estimated mid-year population). Arrows indicate the introduction of new therapeutic agents. Data from National Office of Vital Statistics, U.S.P.H.S.

to slightly over 100 deaths per 100,000 population in 1955. The probable effects of eliminating the primary causes of death among the aged (diseases of the heart, blood vessels, and kidneys, and cancer) have been calculated as adding approximately 10 years to life expectancy.[8] Thus, at age 70, current life expectancy of approximately 10 years would be increased to 20 years. Although it is improbable that these causes of death will ever be entirely eliminated, future research will no doubt result in substantial reductions over present death rates.

Summary.—If past events are any guide to the future, we may expect an increasing number of older persons in the population in the years ahead. However, the increase in birth rate, which has continued at a higher level than predicted in 1940, will add to the total population more dependent children than anticipated, so that the percentage of aged in the population may not increase as much as predicted. Advances in our knowledge of heart disease and cancer may add even more older people to our population. Current trends also indicate greater mobility, with potential concentration of the aged in parts of the country with milder climates.

3

TRENDS IN | EMPLOYMENT AND RETIREMENT

During the past five years, employment of the elderly has received increasing attention. Surveys have shown that older workers are at a disadvantage in the labor market,[1] and a number of suggestions for improving their work opportunities have been made, ranging from proposals in some states for legislation to prohibit discrimination because of age[2] to the establishment of special counseling and placement facilities.[2,3] Although it is recognized that many older people must continue to work for economic reasons, the increasing demands for labor have focused attention on the need to retain experienced and competent older workers in the labor force.[4] The desirability of providing jobs for all who want to continue to work is recognized. The primary problem is to devise objective criteria to decide fairly the question of continued employment for individual workers. Although this problem has been widely discussed,[5] no such objective tests are immediately at hand. The development of objective tests for continued employment is still a research problem that cannot be solved until we know a great deal more about what older people can and cannot do.

Employment aspirations of the elderly.—In our cultural pattern, having a job has important psychological connotations beyond the mere receipt of a pay check. Advancement of the individual, with regard to his economic status as well as to his social prestige, is closely associated with work. Although the individual may state as one of his goals in life the attainment of the ability to retire, he is often unable to accept this role when it is presented to him. In our culture, failure to work, except for reasons of health, is regarded as a sign of weakness. Consequently, there are strong pressures on the individual to continue to work as long as he can, without reference to his economic needs alone. Recent studies have shown that work has a variety of meanings.[6] To some, work is primarily a means of providing income for sustenance. Other values from work include a way of filling the day, or passing time; a source of self-respect and a means of achieving recognition from others; providing social contacts; giving purpose to life; a source of new experiences and opportunity for creativity; and a source of service to others. Individuals from different socio-economic classes view the question of continued employment quite differently. For example, workers at the lower skill and socioeconomic levels regard their work more frequently as merely a way to earn a living and, in general, recognize fewer extrafinancial meanings in their work than do workers of higher skill. Individual interviews were conducted with 128 steelworkers, 186 coal miners, and 64 salesmen and saleswomen, and questionnaires were submitted to 208 skilled craftsmen and 138 physicians, age 65 and above. All five occupational groups obtained values such as social participation, self-respect, and prestige from their work in addition to the earning of money. The strongest desire for continued employment was found among the professional groups, who also reported values in service to others as one of their work satisfactions. Table 2 summarizes the

TABLE 2

PERCENTAGE OF MEN BY OCCUPATIONAL GROUP WHO WANTED TO CONTINUE OR CONTINUED WORK PAST AGE 65*

Occupational Group	Percent
Unskilled and semiskilled steelworkers	32
Coal miners	42†
Skilled craftsmen	49‡
Department-store salesmen	65
Physicians	67‡

* Source: E. A. Friedmann and R. J. Havighurst, *The Meaning of Work and Retirement* (Chicago, University of Chicago Press, 1954), p. 183.

† This figure is probably somewhat higher than it should be when contrasted with the steelworker group. About half of the coal miners studied were already over the optional retirement age of 60; therefore we might expect that many of the men who might have answered "No" to this question had already been selected out by retirement.

‡ These figures are minimal estimates, since in each of these groups an unknown number of men who were not now employed had remained at their jobs past 65. However, the figures for these groups represent the proportion of men over 65 currently employed.

results obtained in this study on the percentage of men who wanted to continue to work past the age of 65. As Dr. Havighurst points out, one of the important trends in the employment of the elderly is the gradual change in the meaning of work. The substitution of other activities which will supply the needs of older people to maintain their self-esteem and their position in the community will have important implications with regard to the desire for employment among older people in the future. These factors will become increasingly important as retirement programs of the future are able to meet the economic needs of older people.

We must, therefore, temper our concept that all people over the age of 65 would wish to continue in employment, particularly if there were no economic necessity for doing so; this is far from saying that aging people wish to attain a life of idleness. Many surveys, conducted in various communities in the United States over the past five years, have indicated a strong desire among the elderly for continued participation in community affairs and in socially important activities.[7] As community education proceeds with the development of programs of activities for older people, there will undoubtedly be some reduction in the pressures for employment.

Employment of the elderly.—In the meantime, however, there are a good many older people who must continue to have work of some kind in order to maintain an adequate income. In addition, the expanding economy has resulted in the need for greater numbers of workers. According to projections made by the Bureau of Labor Statistics, these pressures for increased numbers of workers will continue for some years in the future. Consequently, one of the interesting developments during the past five years has been the shift in emphasis from maintaining older workers in the labor market because of their individual economic needs to a consideration of retaining older workers to meet the demands for an increased labor force. Between 1890 and 1940, the percentage of the total labor force in the United States, aged 65 and over, fluctuated between 4.3 and 4.9 percent for males and between 2.1 and 2.5 percent for females. In 1950, however, 5.5 percent of the male labor force and 3.1 percent of the female labor force were 65 years of age and over.[8] The increased demand for workers has resulted in the retention of more 65-year-olds in the working force. However, over this interval of time, the proportion of the total population over age 65 increased from 4 to 8.2 percent, so that there has been a marked reduction in the percentage of the total number of individuals over age 65 who are still working. Thus, in 1890, of the total male population aged 65 and over, 68.2 percent were still employed, as compared with 38.7 percent in 1954, and an estimated 30.3 percent in 1975. With increased employment among women, the trend since 1890 has been just the reverse. In other words, in 1890 only 7.6 percent of the women aged 65 and over were employed; whereas in 1955, 9.5 percent of the women were working (Table 3). With continued expansion of our economy, the trend is in the direction of increased employment of women at all ages.

TABLE 3

PERCENTAGE OF POPULATION AGED 45 YEARS AND OVER IN THE
LABOR FORCE, 1890–1954*

Age and Sex	1890 (June)	1900 (June)	1920 (Jan.)	1930 (April)	1940 (April)	1950 (April)	1954 (Nov.)	1975 (Est.)
Males								
45–54....	93.9	92.8	93.5	93.8	92.7	91.7	96.7	94.6
55–64....	89.0	86.1	86.3	86.5	84.6	82.9	88.8	82.3
65 and over	68.2	63.2	55.6	54.0	42.2	41.6	40.6	35.3
Females								
45–54....	12.5	14.2	17.9	19.7	22.4	33.0	42.8	52.2
55–64....	11.5	12.6	14.3	15.3	16.6	22.8	31.8	35.4
65 and over	7.6	8.3	7.3	7.3	6.0	7.6	9.5	11.8

* Data from John S. Durand, *The Labor Force in the United States, 1890–1960* (New York, Social Science Research Council, 1948, xviii, 284 pp.); Bureau of the Census, *U.S. Census of Population, 1950*, Preliminary Reports, Series PC-7, No. 2; Bureau of the Census, *Current Population Reports, Labor Force*, Series P-57, No. 149, Dec. 1954.

Analysis of the nature of the employment of older people shows a relative abundance of farmers, proprietors, craftsmen, and service operators. Table 4 shows the percentage distribution in major oc-

TABLE 4
Estimated Percentage Distribution of Employed Males
by Major Occupational Groups

| | 1948* | | 1953† | |
Occupation	Age 14–64 Yrs.	Age 65 Yrs. and Over	Age 14–64 Yrs.	Age 65 Yrs. and Over
Total	100	100	100	100
Professional and semiprofessional workers	6	6	8	7
Farmers and farm managers	11	26	8	20
Proprietors, managers, officials, except farm	13	15	12	14
Clerical, sales, and kindred workers	12	7	12	10
Craftsmen, foremen, and kindred workers	19	13	20	14
Operators and kindred workers	21	9	22	9
Service workers	6	11	6	14
Farm laborers and foremen	4	5	4	4
Laborers, except farm and mine	8	8	8	8

* Unpublished data from sample survey by the Bureau of the Census.

† Bureau of the Census, *Current Population Reports, Labor Force*, Series P-57, No. 130, Table 13; and Metropolitan Life Insurance Co., *Statistical Bulletin*, 35: 3, 1954.

cupational groups of workers over 65 in 1948 as compared with 1953. In both years, the maximum employment of older men was on the farm. However, even between 1948 and 1953, there has been a decrease in the proportion of farm workers. Between 1948 and 1953, there has been an increase in clerical, sales, and kindred workers and service operators among the elderly, which has been greater than the increment in employment of these groups in the total population. Although less than 1 percent of males over age 65 were employed as private household workers, 25 percent of females fell in this category, with an additional 20 percent of the women employed as service workers. Recent studies have shown that continuation of employment after age 65 is related to the nature of the occupation. Thus, Clark and Dunn[9] found that among watchmakers, precious metal workers, and musical instrument makers, for example, the percentage of workers who continued employment after age 65 is 75–85 percent as contrasted with only 5–15 percent for coal miners and railway signalmen. Thus, the physical demands of an occupation may play a role in determining continued employment.

Unemployment.—Unemployment is more prevalent among older workers than among younger. Furthermore, the older workers remain unemployed longer on the average than the younger ones. Table 5 summarizes the results of the Bureau of Employment Security survey covering 42,000 workers who were seeking jobs in early 1950. It is apparent that the number of short-term unemployed falls

TABLE 5

PERCENTAGE OF JOB APPLICANTS BY PERIOD OF TIME UNEMPLOYED
AND BY AGE GROUP, IN THREE AREAS, 1950*

Age Group	Houston (3–5% Unemployed)	Lancaster (3–5% Unemployed)	Columbus (5–7% Unemployed)
Less Than Four Weeks Spent Seeking Employment			
Total	22.1	26.6	24.3
Under 20	35.6†	33.1	33.7
20 to 24	26.3‡	32.2	27.5
25 to 44	23.0	28.7	26.1
45 to 64	16.2	24.7	18.8
65 and over	7.5	14.6	18.0
More Than Twenty Weeks Spent Seeking Employment			
Total	10.1	15.4	17.5
Under 20	5.3†	8.1	11.4
20 to 24	8.6‡	9.8	10.5
25 to 44	8.6	13.1	17.2
45 to 64	13.3	19.1	22.4
65 and over	26.8	24.9	23.4

* Source: R. K. Burns and L. B. Brown, "The Older Worker in Industry," in A. I. Lansing (ed.), *Cowdry's Problems of Ageing* (3d ed.; Baltimore, Williams & Wilkins, 1952), pp. 983–1018.
† Includes applicants under 21 years of age.
‡ Includes applicants 21 to 24 years of age.

consistently with age, whereas the long-term jobless become more numerous in the higher age categories. Small increases in the general level of employment produce a disproportionate increase in short-term unemployment in the older age groups. In a recently completed survey of employment experience in seven major labor markets in the United States, it was found that the severest impact of unemployment fell on workers who were 65 or more years of age.[10] In every occupational group and in every industry division, there were substantially more workers in this age category on a relative basis who were unemployed than employed. For the seven areas as a whole (Detroit, Los Angeles, Miami, Minneapolis–St. Paul, Philadelphia, Seattle, and Worcester, Massachusetts), the 65-year age group accounted for 10 percent of the jobless but for no more than 3 percent of the employed. Once employed, an older worker was more stable in his employment than the young. Older workers, that is, over the age of 45, held about 35 percent of the jobs, but they experienced less than one-fourth of the annual total separations. They quit their jobs less than half as often as the younger workers. It was also clear that older workers had a better chance of getting a job with a small firm than with a large one. It was more likely for an older worker to be hired in a job which was not covered by private pension plan than one in which such coverage was available. Workers 45 years of age and over accounted for 25 percent of the hiring in employment without pension plans as contrasted with 14 percent in jobs with this advantage. It is therefore apparent that job opportunities diminish for older workers and that the effects of general unemployment are felt most acutely by older workers.

Reasons for retirement.—As industrialization proceeds in association with expanded social security coverage and additional private pension programs, more and more workers are faced with compulsory retirement at some specified chronological age. However, the high level of employment during the past decade has permitted some degree of selectivity and choice for the individual with regard to retirement. Studies made by the Federal Security Agency on the reasons for retirement among old-age insurance beneficiaries indicate clearly that the motives underlying retirement are influenced by a variety

TABLE 6

PERCENTAGE DISTRIBUTION OF RETIRED WORKERS AT END OF SURVEY YEAR 1951, BY REASON FOR TERMINATION OF LAST COVERED EMPLOYMENT BEFORE FIRST BENEFIT PAYMENT, BY ELIGIBILITY STATUS AND YEAR OF FIRST BENEFIT*

Reason for Termination of Employment	Total	1939 Eligibles† Whose First Benefit Payment Was in:							1950 Eligibles‡
		Total	1940–41	1942–43	1944–45	1946–47	1948–49	1950	
Retired men workers									
Number	12,081	10,686	782	663	1,408	2,876	3,485	1,472	1,395
Total percent	100.0	100.0	100.0	100.0	100.0	100.0	100.0	100.0	100.0
Quit job	55.3	55.1	52.7	61.5	63.7	54.1	52.9	52.6	56.2
Unable to work§	41.5	41.5	37.7	45.6	48.1	40.8	40.2	39.9	41.4
Retired voluntarily in good health‖	3.9	4.2	5.1	5.7	5.6	3.8	3.7	3.3	1.6
For other kind of job‖ ..	4.1	3.8	4.1	4.2	4.7	3.8	3.3	3.4	6.6
Other**	5.8	5.7	5.8	6.0	5.3	5.6	5.7	5.9	6.6
Lost job	44.7	44.9	47.3	38.5	36.3	45.9	47.1	47.4	43.8
Job discontinued††	20.9	19.7	16.2	18.3	18.3	20.0	21.2	19.7	29.5
Reached company retirement age	10.9	12.1	15.7	9.4	9.1	12.7	11.9	13.6	1.2
Considered unable to work by employer	6.7	6.8	9.3	5.9	4.8	6.8	6.9	7.4	6.0
Other‡‡	6.3	6.2	6.0	5.0	4.1	6.4	7.0	6.7	7.1

* Source: *Social Security Bulletin*, **18**:7, May 1955.

† Beneficiaries whose benefits were awarded under the 1939 amendments to the Social Security Act.

‡ Beneficiaries whose benefits were awarded for September 1950 under the 1950 amendments to the Social Security Act.

§ Beneficiaries who quit because of sickness or accident or because they were tired or thought that their work was too hard for them or that they were too old to continue working.

‖ Number reporting on all items in this table. Because the number reporting on different combinations of items varies slightly from one table to another, there may be slight variations in numbers and percentages that apparently should be the same.

¶ Beneficiaries entitled in September 1950. Effective that month, the retirement test was liberalized to permit fully insured workers aged 75 and over to receive benefits regardless of earnings and those aged 65–74 to receive benefits if covered earnings were no more than $50 a month. Before September 1950 the maximum amount of covered wages permitted without suspension of benefits was $14.99 for all beneficiaries.

** Beneficiaries who quit after a quarrel with the employer or fellow employees, during a strike, because they were unwilling to adjust to another kind of assigned work, or were needed at home, and so forth.

†† Beneficiaries who retired in good health to have more leisure or because they thought they had worked long enough.

‡‡ Beneficiaries who quit a full-time covered job hoping to find a different kind of work or to take a part-time covered job or noncovered employment.

of factors. Table 6 shows the reason for termination of the last covered employment before entitlement in male old-age insurance beneficiaries between 1940 and 1950. This table shows clearly that only 4–5 percent of workers retired voluntarily while they were in good health. Voluntary retirements were at a maximum in 1940–45 and have been decreasing since then, even though the benefits available to the retired worker have increased (see Chapter 4). One-third to one-half of the group apparently retired for reasons of health, whereas only 10–15 percent of the group reached the company retirement age. The scanty data that we have point up some glaring inconsistencies between the reported voluntary retirement (4–5 percent of retirees) and the expressed desire of employees to continue working (30–70 percent). It appears that many elderly people who say they wish to continue working are, in the eyes of their employer, incapable of doing so because of poor health. We do not yet have any adequate estimates of health status of the older age group that permit us to decide between the claim that few of those aged 65 and above are physically able to work[11] and the claim that a very high proportion of retirees prefer to continue in gainful employment.[12] With authorization by the last Congress for periodic health surveys to be made on a nation-wide basis, we can look forward to obtaining more specific information on this important question within the next few years.

Adequacy of older workers.—A number of surveys of both local and national scope have brought to light conflicting evidence with regard to age and employment policies. In opinion surveys, personnel managers in general maintain that policies of their respective companies do not discriminate against employment because of age. The facts of unemployment and difficulties of older workers to secure new positions speak to the contrary. In a survey of 1,000 employers, the New York State Joint Legislative Committee on Problems of the Aging[13] found that industry rates them as more loyal and steadfast and as productive as their juniors. Three out of four employers who were interviewed believed that older workers produced as much as the younger ones. A similar survey made by the California Department of Industrial Relations[14] showed that, among the employers questioned, age had little relation to efficiency, although some jobs were believed more appropriate for older men. Many employers stated that they preferred the older workers in jobs calling for experience and judgment and on jobs where quality was more important than speed. Similar replies from supervisors were obtained in a more recent survey conducted by the Bureau of Business Management of the University of Illinois among industrial, retailing, office, and managerial personnel.[15] Other studies have shown that in spite of certain biases in opinions about older workers,[16] they are often capable in the performance of their duties.[17] In spite of these expressed opinions of preferences for older workers in some jobs, the practice of personnel officers is apt to discriminate against them.

Some data are available on other qualities of older workers.[18] For instance, records show that absenteeism is generally less frequent among older than younger workers. Among men, absenteeism was highest among workers under 20 (an average of 5.2 days lost per 100 scheduled work days), after which it declined steadily until a low point was reached in the 55–59 age group (2.8 days lost). There was a slight increase in the rate for men over 65, but even this compared favorably with the absenteeism of the men in their thirties and forties, and was considerably less than for men in their twenties and teens. Likewise, among women, the lowest absentee rate was in the group aged 55–59.

It is often claimed that older workers are more liable to injury and require a longer time to recuperate from disabling illnesses than do younger workers. The facts do not bear out this belief. Injuries which required an employee to miss at least one full work shift occurred 9.7 times per million hours of work for all age groups, but only 7.8 times for the age group 50–54 and 10.1 times for those 55–59. No age group over 50 had a rate as high as the group aged 33–44. In the case of nondisabling injuries which required only first aid, the frequency rates for all groups of workers over the age of 50 ranged from one-half to one-fourth of the rate for workers in their twenties. Although older workers required more time for their injuries to heal, the lower incidence resulted in less loss of time for the older group than for the younger employees. There is, then, no substance to the belief that the hiring of older workers will increase accident rates and disability insurance costs.[19]

Job counseling and placement services for older workers.—A great deal has been done in the past few years with regard to publicizing the employability of older workers, and in a number of cities special counseling services and placement agencies for older workers have been set up. In New York State, Michigan, and Chicago, for example, it has been shown that through counseling of individual workers and special efforts in placement, a significantly greater number of elderly workers can secure gainful employment.[20] This, in itself, offers some objective proof that discrimination in employment, based on age, is a fact of our present culture. The goal for the future is to determine effective ways of breaking down and eliminating this discrimination. One proposal made by the New York State Joint Legislative Committee on Problems of the Aging is the enactment of specific anti-discrimination laws.[21] It is argued that enactment of such laws will remove the current sanction of discrimination as a legitimate employment practice. It will force unrealistic personnel policies to be re-examined. On the other hand, it may be argued that social changes are more apt to be acceptable when based on community education rather than forced through legal devices.

One of the great unknowns is a precise determination of the number of people over the age of 65 who are still physically able to work, the number who want to work, and the number who find continued employment necessary because of inadequacies in the pension payments available to them. We also need to know the limitations of older people with respect to performance. With detailed analyses of the requirements of various occupations, it would be possible to determine the type of jobs most appropriate for older workers with a given degree of disability.

Although 60–65 percent of those over the age of 65 have some physical disability, only about 10 percent are actually incapacitated. Since only about 5 percent of the aged retire voluntarily while in good health, we may regard something of the order of 80–85 percent of the aged males as potential candidates for employment of some kind.

At the present time, we know that approximately 60 percent of the males over the age of 65 are actually employed. Thus, the remaining 20–25 percent, who are presumably physically capable of some form of work, represent the group that contribute heavily to the unemployed. At least half of the workers who are retired at age 65 because of current employment practices would prefer to continue working. It is this group which may be greatly augmented in times of reduced economic activity that requires special consideration.

Age changes in capacity for work.—Although much remains to be learned, research over the past few years has provided data which must be brought to bear upon any consideration of the employment of older people. First of all, we now know that with increasing age there is a gradual reduction in the reserve capacities of many organ systems in the body.[22] Practically, this means that the potentialities for recuperation and for meeting periods of stress and maximum activity are less in the older individual than in the young. Thus, there is a gradual reduction in sensory acuity, muscular strength, and the general ability to readjust to a physiological stress, whether it be a demand for increased performance or the combating of a disease process. It is also clear that there is a gradual reduction in the speed of performance with increasing age.[23] This means that the older individual will perform less effectively in any operation that must be completed in a specified time span. On the positive side of the ledger, however, it has been shown that in operations that are well practiced, there is very little decrement with age.[24] In fact, in tasks requiring care and accuracy, the total effective output of the older person oftentimes exceeds that of the young. In our present economy, very few jobs tax the physical capacities of workers. Thus, these reductions in performance ability with age do not seem to be crucial. The loss of speed of performance with age can become a limiting factor in some types of employment.

Throughout the country, there is a rising distrust of chronological age as the sole determinant of time of retirement. The magical age of 65 has, for its defense, only the ease of administration and the fact that it has become incorporated into our social security system and other retirement benefits which came into being at a time when the general policy was to remove as many people as possible from the labor force. None of the research studies on the physiological or psychological characteristics of aging people offer any evidence that sudden changes in performance or capacities occur at any chronological age. Whatever decrements that occur seem to take place gradually over the age span from 30 up to 90 years. This is not to say that individuals may not go downhill rapidly after some specific age. However, an answer to this question cannot be made until we have studies with repeated measurements on the same person as he grows older.

Criteria for continued employment.—In the face of an expanding economy with the need for more and more workers, attention has been focused on criteria for continuing employment rather than for its termination. These circumstances have been helpful in advancing the policies of labor unions, which are in general opposed to fixed retirement ages. Some recently negotiated contracts explicitly exclude forced retirement based on chronological age alone. Instead, evaluation of job performance and health status is required for each worker prior to retirement. Labor unions have, by means of seniority clauses in management-union contracts, protected their older members from discrimination in general layoffs. The seniority principle means that preference in promotions, better assignments, and re-employment after layoff depend primarily on the number of years of service. The difficulty with seniority provisions is that, while they grant preference to long-time employees, they also obstruct employment of young and old workers who do not have seniority with a particular plant or union.

Some union agreements specifically require employment of a certain number of older workers. The agreement found in some building trades requires at least one worker aged 55 or over among every five, seven, or ten journeymen employed.

Although unions insist on rigid adherence to the wage standards agreed upon for all regular employees, many of them will permit an older worker to take a lower-rated job at a lower wage scale. Only about one-third of the international unions refuse to permit such downgrading. Some agreements specify a minimum rate below which wages of substandard workers may not fall. Aged workers who are unable to perform their regular work are sometimes assured transfers to other types of work by management-union contracts. Unions are, in general, opposed to part-time employment of retired workers.

Although all of these devices may aid in maintaining employment of the elderly, they break down in times of severe unemployment. Businesses fail, new inventions render old occupations obsolete, layoffs do occur, and attachments to previous jobs are broken. The longterm solution of the problem requires the development of jobs which can be filled by older workers.

If chronological age is to be abandoned as a criterion for retirement, it is obvious that some other objective criteria should be substituted, if at all possible. The concept of physiological age has been an attractive one, and it has been hoped that some battery of tests could be assembled which would give objective evidence of the physiological or psychological status of the individual at a given time. However, at the present time, we do not know enough about changes that take place with aging in normal persons to be able to devise such an index with any assurance. Research has shown rather clearly that aging does not proceed uniformly with respect to all organ systems in the same individual. Consequently, any physiological index must either be based on a wide variety of tests or there must be separate scores devised for various organ systems. We must also have a great deal more information about the role of the specific organ system either in the maintenance of the health of the individual or with respect to the requirements of a specific job situation. Researchers are striving to assemble information which will ultimately permit the development of such tests of physiological or psychological age.

Flexible retirement plans.—Experience in some manufacturing plants has shown that a flexible retirement policy can be developed and administered. Although health status plays an important role in determining employability, it is obvious that other factors must be taken into consideration. Thus, in some plants, a worker reaching the age of 65 is evaluated and a final judgment is reached in consultations between the worker's supervisor, his physician, a representative of management, and a representative of his labor union.[25] In this way, workers who wish to remain on the job and who can perform effectively are retained in the labor pool. With effective preretirement counseling, workers can accept the decisions of the group with a minimum of trauma.

Current research on the physiological and psychological characteristics of aging people indicates that, for many of them, a plan of gradual retirement over a period of years would offer distinct advantages. Programs of gradual retirement whereby the older worker gradually begins to relinquish responsibilities, reducing his working time so that his retirement is spread out over a period of three to five years, have been discussed. During this period of partial retirement, the person is able to develop additional interests outside of his job and thus is better prepared to continue an active life than if he had been confronted with a sudden termination of all of his job responsibilities. Studies have shown that this is actually what happens among self-employed professional people who have successfully adjusted to retirement. It is obvious that programs of this kind must be highly individualized and will perhaps work best among university, managerial, and supervisory personnel. Although many practical problems are involved, it seems clear that programs of this kind would be of benefit not only to the individual, but also to society as a whole in that effective productivity would be maintained.

Extending employment of the elderly.—Much can be done in fitting jobs to the capabilities of the older worker.[26] For example, the use of conveyors and mechanical contrivances has done much to remove the elements of manual labor from many operations, thus permitting continued employment of older people. The introduction of shorter hours, the slowing of assembly lines, and even the redesign of machinery may go a long way toward retaining older people in employment. A number of industrial plants have found ways of utilizing older workers. For example, in some companies, older workers have been found to be quite adequate in maintaining machine operations when teamed up with the younger worker to aid in the setup. Some companies have found effective use for older workers on a part-time basis. For example, the Joa Company has set up branch offices in Florida where retired engineers, draftsmen, and the like are regularly employed on either a full- or part-time basis.[27] Throughout the country, other examples of special industries catering to older workers might be mentioned. In Boston, Sunset Industries, Inc., has been established to provide facilities for the creative employment of men and women over 60 years of age. A number of outstanding business and industrial firms in Massachusetts offer subcontracts to Sunset Industries. In Florida, the Bryant Furniture Company produces Early American furniture in a small shop employing eight full-time retired craftsmen. In Schenectady, New York, four retired engineers incorporated as the Mohawk Development Service subcontract drafting from other industries. They have hired as many as 49 retired draftsmen to carry on the work, under very flexible work schedules. Originally organized in 1938, the Forty Plus Club has successfully aided in the re-employment of white-collar and professional workers from the higher-income group. To qualify for membership, the applicant must (1) be over 40 years of age, (2) be an American citizen, (3) have earned a substantial income in an executive capacity, (4) have acceptable experience and educational backgrounds, (5) have high moral character, and (6) have proved ability, performance, and accomplishment. Before being accepted for membership, all applicants are interviewed by appropriate committees made up of experts from business and industry. After the capacities of the applicants are carefully evaluated, interviews with prospective employers are arranged. At the present time, over 80 percent of the applicants who have been accepted in the Club have been placed in executive positions to the satisfaction of themselves and their employers.

In at least three cities, retired business and professional men have formed organizations to pool their experience and offer it where needed in the community. Three of these organizations are Management Counselors, Inc., of New York, Consulting and Adviser Services of Wilmington, Delaware, and Experience, Inc., of St. Louis. The St. Louis organization is composed of 42 former executives who claim to have 2,000 years of experience in their membership. Originally conceived as a venture for providing meaningful activity for retired individuals, the group has found effective outlets for its talents in providing consultative services to small business in the St. Louis area. Members have also helped to investigate the operation of the St.

Louis Board of Education, have served on the Off-Street Parking Commission, the Community Chest, grand juries, and other local and state civic and charitable agencies.

By following the common policy of requiring complete retirement at a fixed chronological age, our universities are discarding many people who are of great value to society. While it is true that some older people take teaching positions in smaller colleges when they are retired from large universities, many are lost to our educational system. Some professional societies, such as the American Psychological Association[28] and the American Physiological Society,[29] have set up special committees to aid in placing retired professors in teaching and research positions. With the rising need for teachers and research workers, further expansion of such programs should occur. Perhaps a better approach would be for universities and colleges to assume leadership in developing more imaginative and flexible retirement programs.

Although the newspaper reports about Aunt Sarah, who at the age of 65 began to make currant jelly in her kitchen and built it into a $100,000-a-year industry, make exciting reading, it is cruel to imply that everyone can go into business for himself on retirement. Self-employment is only one of the ways to maintain activity and income among the elderly. While everything possible to encourage such activities should be done, we must not fail to explore other plans and programs for continuing employment among those who wish to work.

Hovering over all projections and plans for the future employment of older people is the cloud of automation in industry. No one can predict, with any degree of certainty, what automation will do to employment of the elderly.[30] On the one hand, the reduction in physical activity may make it possible for workers to retain their jobs of attending machines to a more advanced age. On the other hand, if jobs demand simultaneous monitoring of a number of dials and instruments, with quick responses on the part of the worker, the older person will certainly be at a disadvantage. These are questions which can be answered only with time.

Summary.—Although the total labor force of the United States is made up of slightly more older workers than before, the population aged 65 and over has increased at a more rapid rate than employment, so that the percent of the age group 65 and over remaining in employment is still falling in the case of males. Increased demands for workers have resulted in the continued employment of more elderly women than before. However, there has been an increased realization that many workers are still competent at the age of 65 and beyond, and special programs for counseling and placement of older workers have demonstrated their effectiveness. Impaired health status is a primary factor in stimulating retirement. A number of plans in operation have shown that compulsory retirement at a fixed chronological age is not the only solution. It is becoming increasingly apparent that the problem of employment of the elderly cannot be met by businessmen and employers alone. The worker himself has a responsibility to accept different kinds of work, to accept willingly changes in pay for such work, and to undertake any training or retraining which may be required to maintain his employability. A community itself has a great responsibility for providing facilities for assisting industry and workers to make these adaptations. The lack of job-counseling services for older workers and of retraining programs is still a problem, although pilot studies have adequately demonstrated their effectiveness. We also need a reorientation of people generally and a change in the current concept that the social usefulness of an individual can be measured only in terms of paid employment. People must be made to realize that there are many activities of great benefit to the community that can be performed by retired people without monetary reward. Programs whereby older people can make an effective contribution to the community need to be extended.

4

TRENDS IN | INCOME MAINTENANCE

The provision of economic security to aged people raises problems that affect the entire country. For improvement in the economic position of the aged group there is required either a redistribution of the total productivity of the country, which means that some groups of the population will receive less income than at present, or an increase in total productivity in goods and services. During the past five years, there have been vast changes in both the sources and the amount of income available to the aged. However, we must remember that economic status is measured not by dollar income alone, but by the amount of goods and services that the dollars will buy. In September 1956, the Consumer Price Index, compiled by the Bureau of Labor Statistics, stood at 117.1. This means that a benefit payment of $50 in 1955 was required to purchase the same goods and services that could be bought with a payment of $26.50 in 1940.[1]

Income level of the aged.—With our expanding economy of the past ten years, coupled with changes in social security, there have been improvements in the economic status of the aged. In 1948, approximately 3.5 million (32 percent) of the total 11.5 million persons aged 65 and over in the United States had no money income of their own during the year. As shown in Table 7, by 1954 only about 24 percent of the population over age 65 received no income. Since the number of aged had increased from 11.5 million to 13.6 million, there were still about 3.25 million aged without income. The table also shows that in 1948 more women (50.6 percent) were without income than men (10.9 percent). By 1954, only 7.6 percent of the men had no income, but 37.8 percent of the women fell in this category. The economic status of women improved more than that of men. Table 7 shows that even after adjustments for the rise in prices

TABLE 7

Percentage Distribution of Persons Aged 65 and Over, by Sex and by Money Income, 1948 and 1954*

Annual Money Income	Total			Men			Women		
	1948	1954		1948	1954		1948	1954	
		1948 Prices†	Current Prices		1948 Prices†	Current Prices		1948 Prices†	Current Prices
Total number‡ (in thousands)	11,590	13,630		5,500	6,340		6,100	7,290	
Less than $1,000§	73.7	69.0	66.6	55.6	50.5	46.8	89.9	85.2	83.7
0	31.8	23.8	23.8	10.9	7.6	7.6	50.6	37.8	37.8
$1–499	21.1	22.2	18.2	20.7	18.9	14.3	21.4	25.2	21.6
500–999	20.6	23.0	23.9	23.7	24.0	23.5	17.8	22.2	24.2
1,000–1,499	8.5	8.9	9.4	12.7	12.5	13.1	4.6	5.8	6.2
1,500–1,999	4.6	6.0	5.9	7.3	9.5	9.0	2.2	3.5	3.3
2,000–2,999	6.8	7.1	7.7	12.3	11.8	12.6	1.7	2.6	3.4
3,000–4,999	4.3	6.1	6.9	8.1	10.6	12.4	1.0	1.9	2.0
5,000 and over	2.2	2.9	3.6	3.9	5.1	6.1	.5	1.0	1.4

* Source: *Social Security Bulletin*, **19** : 9, April 1956.

† Estimated roughly in the Division of Research and Statistics by converting the limits of each income class in 1954 to 1948 dollars on the basis of the change in the BLS consumer price index and then recalculating the number of persons at each revised income level.

‡ Estimated number at the survey dates, April 1949 and April 1955, respectively. April 1949 estimates adjusted to conform to the most recent population estimates.

§ Includes a small number of persons who reported a net loss for the year. The proportion with zero income is probably overstated.

between 1948 and 1954, there has been a slight improvement in income levels among the aged. Between 1948 and 1952, the median income for aged men with income increased from about $1,000 to $1,247; this was still considerably less than the median income for males aged 55 to 64, which in 1952 was $3,105.[2] Thus, it is clear that although the income level for older people has increased, it is still lower than the average for the general population.

Income requirements of the aged.—Since older people have fewer family responsibilities, their economic needs may be substantially less than workers in the middle-aged brackets. The U.S. Department of Labor has periodically made estimates of yearly costs for elderly couples to maintain their health and normal participation in community life. Although costs vary somewhat in terms of geography ($1,908 per year in Milwaukee to $1,614 in Scranton, Pennsylvania, in 1950),[3] Table 8 summarizes estimates made in 1951 for total maintenance costs for couples, single males, and single females living in cities and on farms. The last column of the table shows the percent

TABLE 8

Sample Budgets for Total Maintenance of Aged Individuals
Not Living with Relatives*

(1951 Dollars)

	Total Maintenance Costs	Percent with Income Below This Level
Couples		
Urban	$1,850	45–50
Farm	925–1,250	27–31
Single males		
Urban	1,125	52–58
Farm	550–750	33–36
Single females		
Urban	1,075	71–75

* Data from P. O. Steiner, "The Size, Nature and Adequacy of the Resources of the Aged," *American Economic Review,* **44**: 645–60, 1954. Consumer prices to moderate income, urban families increased from 111.0 in 1951 to 114.8 in 1954.

of individuals over the age of 65 who, in 1952, were receiving incomes less than the estimated amounts required. It is apparent that at least half of the aged group living in cities received incomes less than the estimated requirements, as compared with one-third of those living on farms.

Sources of income to the aged.—There have also been major shifts in the sources of income of the elderly. Table 9 compares the sources of income estimated in December 1949, June 1954, and June 1956. Although such estimates are subject to a fair degree of error because of the inability to determine the extent to which income is received from more than one source by an individual, and the difficulties in obtaining data on insurance annuities, payments from private retirement systems, investments, and other types of savings, the data are adequate to identify the major sources of income. First of all, there has been a marked increase in the number of aged receiving their income from social insurance. In 1948, there were about the same number of aged receiving income from employment as from social insurance. In 1956, almost twice as many individuals received their income from social insurance as from employment. There has also been a substantial decrease in the number of individuals without income. By June 1956, there were 4.1 million men, or 61.8 percent, and 3.9 million women, or 50.3 percent, over age 65 who were receiving benefits from social insurance and related programs. In 1956, almost 2 million of the 14.5 million over 65 were receiving benefits from more than one of the sources specified in Table 9. The primary trend in income maintenance has been a rapid rise in dependence upon Old-Age and Survivors Insurance. Continued employment still offers higher income levels to the aged than any retirement program, and more elderly were employed in 1956 than in 1948. However, in the future, more and more people will be dependent on retirement payments after age 65 or 70.

Although we must continue to make every effort to provide employment for older individuals who wish to work, it is probable that more and more people will wish to retire from the labor market. This trend will be abetted by increasing retirement benefits to the point where elderly couples can live adequately on the payments, and it will

TABLE 9

Sources of Income of the Aged*

Source of Income	December 1949†			June 1954‡			June 1956§		
	Total	Men	Women	Total	Men	Women	Total	Men	Women
Total population aged 65 and over.....	11.0	5.2	5.8	13.7	6.3	7.2	14.5	6.7	7.8
No income.................	3.5	.5	3.0	3.3	.4	2.9	1.5	.1	1.4
Employment................	3.8	2.4	1.4	3.9	2.4	1.5	4.3	2.6	1.7
Earners.................	2.9	2.4	.5	3.0	2.4	.6	3.3	2.6	.7
Wives of earners............	.9	...	.9	.9	...	.9	.9	...	.9
Social insurance and related programs.	3.0	1.7	1.3	6.2	3.3	2.9	8.0	4.1	3.9
Old-Age and Survivors Insurance...	1.9	1.1	.8	4.9	2.6	2.3	6.6	3.4	3.2
Railroad Retirement	.3	.2	.1	.5	.3	.2	.5	.3	.2
Federal Civil Service Retirement....	.1	.1	‖	.4	.2	.2	.5	.3	.2
Veterans programs	.3	.2	.1	.4	.3	.1	.7	.5	.2
Others	.4	.1	.3	.1	.1	‖	...	...	...
Old-Age Assistance	2.7	1.3	1.4	2.5	1.0	1.5	2.5	1.0	1.5

Numbers (in millions)

* An unknown number of individuals receive incomes from more than one of the sources listed. Hence the sum of all sources of income gives a total greater than the number of individuals actually receiving some income. In 1954 over a million individuals received income from more than one source listed.

† Data from *Social Security Bulletin*, **13**: 15, June 1950.

‡ Data from *Social Security Bulletin*, **17**: 16, December 1954.

§ Data from *Social Security Bulletin*, **19**: 14, December 1956.

‖ Less than 500,000.

also be implemented by changes in our cultural pattern which will encourage aging people to develop community activities that are outside of their working careers. For example, surveys of men receiving old-age benefits in 1940 indicated that only about one in 20 stopped work voluntarily while he was still in good health. In 1954, interviews with retired workers showed that 10–12 percent of clerical, sales, and managerial workers retired voluntarily in order to have more time for themselves. With the development of preretirement programs, it is quite possible that an increasing number of aging workers will seek voluntary retirement in the years to come.[4]

Private pension plans. — The first private pension plan in the United States was set up by the American Express Company, now the Railway Express Agency, in 1875. Over the years, additional concerns established programs so that, in 1930, approximately 725 such plans, covering 2.4 million workers, were in effect. Most of the early plans were noncontributory and unfunded, and carefully avoided the establishment of any "rights" of the worker. The pension was usually awarded at the discretion of management and was considered a gratuity. Pensions could usually be terminated or reduced at will. Gradually, the legal character of pension plans has changed, particularly in the last 20 years, until today practically all pension plans are nondiscriminatory and are considered a right of the employee who meets the eligibility conditions. This important change in philosophy of pensions and pension rights has continued up to the present, with the growth in plans and individual workers covered, as shown in Table 10. A part of this growth in private plans occurred during World War II because of the special conditions growing out of the war economy. Cash wages were frozen and pensions were one of the few ways left open to employers to grant increases in compensation and to compete with each other for labor. Moreover, the establishment of pensions was made relatively inexpensive because of the operation of the excess profits tax. For firms in the higher tax brackets, money put into a pension plan actually cost the company only about 20 cents on the dollar. Since 1949, the growth in coverage under the private plans can be traced, to a considerable extent, to the drive of big labor unions. This growth in private plans has taken place

TABLE 10

ESTIMATED NUMBER OF PRIVATE RETIREMENT PLANS
AND COVERAGE, 1930–1951*

Year	Number of Plans	Number of Persons Covered (millions)
1930	720	2.4
1935	1,090	2.6
1940	1,965	3.7
1945	7,425	5.6
1950	12,330	8.6
1951	14,000	9.6

* Data from U.S. Congress, Joint Committee on the Economic Report by the National Planning Association, *Pensions in the United States* (Washington, D.C., Government Printing Office, 1952, 106 pp.).

parallel with the growth in the social security program. One of the important philosophies expressed by labor leaders is that private plans, obtained in the negotiation of labor contracts, should be developed to supplement the basic payments available through Old-Age and Survivors Insurance. Many of the existing private pension plans are being liberalized and new ones are being established.[5] Although the picture is bright in terms of the number of workers covered, it must be recognized that these plans contribute nothing to the income of workers who have already retired and have relatively little importance for income payments to individuals who will retire within the next 5–10 years, since most of the plans gear benefits to length of employment and to wage level.

The questions of funding these pension plans and the method of contributing to them have been the subject of considerable discussion among economists, at a theoretical level, and between labor and management in terms of practicalities. Labor is anxious to see all private pension plans based on sound actuarial practices, with annual payments into the fund by management. In some contracts, the total contribution to the program has been by management.[6] Labor leaders believe that for protection of the workers, employers should invest pension funds on an annual basis in order to prevent the loss of benefits in case of failure of individual small businesses.

One of the difficulties of private pension plans is that continuity of employment in a given industry, and oftentimes in a given plant, is necessary for a worker to receive retirement benefits. While it is true that in some plans the worker may retain his rights after 5 or 10 years of employment, the general procedure is that if he changes jobs, he loses whatever contribution has been made by the employer. If vesting rights were available in all pension plans, one of the arguments often used by management against hiring middle-aged workers would be removed. With increasing pressures by labor unions, it is probable that more retirement plans, with such vesting rights, will be negotiated in the future.

Old-Age and Survivors Insurance.—The Old-Age and Survivors Insurance program, established by Congress in 1935, has developed into the bulwark of economic security for older people. Over the years, successive amendments have increased coverage from 23.8 million workers in 1940 to 72.1 million in 1955, and have raised the benefits available. Far-reaching changes were brought about by the amendments of 1954, which extended coverage to approximately 10 million persons (6 million on a compulsory basis, 4 million elective) not previously included. The largest groups brought into the system in 1954 were farmers, members of state and local government retirement systems (under voluntary agreement), additional farm and domestic workers, ministers and members of religious orders (on a voluntary basis), and self-employed members of specified professions.[7] In 1956, in addition to admitting certain groups of previously excluded self-employed professional persons (other than doctors of medicine), coverage on a contributory basis was extended, effective January 1, 1957, to nearly 3 million members of the uniformed services.[8] The major groups that remain outside the system are most federal civilian employees now under retirement systems, policemen and firemen covered by a state or local retirement system, physicians, low-income self-employed persons, and farm and domestic workers not regularly employed. By 1957, about 92 out of every 100 jobs were covered under Old-Age and Survivors Insurance on a contributory basis. Since a significant proportion of the excluded groups have other retirement programs, we are approaching the goal of having some pension benefits available for every worker in the United States.

As shown in Figure 7, there has been a marked increment in the

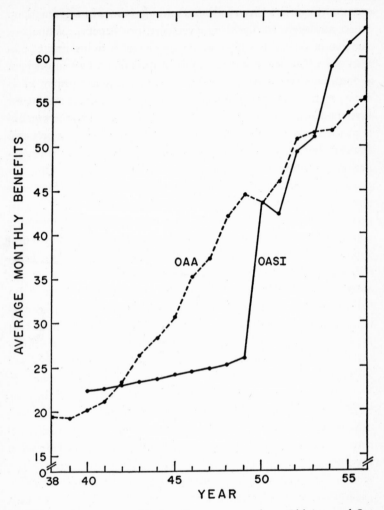

Fig. 7—Average monthly benefits per person from Old-Age and Survivors Insurance and Old-Age Assistance, 1938–1956. Data from *Social Security Bulletin,* Annual Statistical Supplement, 1956.

average monthly payments to individuals under Old-Age and Survivors Insurance. In January 1957, the average payment to the retired worker was $63.14 per month with an additional $33.76 paid to the wife or husband of the retired worker. This amount still falls short of the minimum estimated requirements for adequate maintenance of a household, but it is still considerably better than the average payments of $22.60 per month available in 1940. A part of this increase is due, of course, to maturation of the system, but the greatest increments in benefits were the result of changes in legislation. In the first place, the total annual earnings on which benefits and contributions are based was raised from $3,600 to $4,200 by the amendments of 1954. To overcome the handicap of late entry into the system, the new law also provided that up to five years of the lowest earnings (or no earnings) could be dropped in computing the average income upon which benefits are based. In addition, the minimum benefit for individuals already receiving benefits was raised to $30 per month with a maximum of $98.50. For those coming on the rolls after September 1954, the range of possible benefits was from $30 to $108.50 for an individual and up to $200 for a family. Thus, under the new law, the married worker with an average monthly wage of $350 is eligible for benefits of $162.80 upon retirement, as compared with the maximum of $127.50 under the old law. Of added value to the aged was the provision that retirees may now earn up to $1,200 per year without loss of benefits. One month's benefit is now withheld for each $80 or for each fraction of that amount in excess of $1,200. Older people are now able to take intermittent full-time work, or more regular part-time work, without the loss of benefits. A beneficiary may work throughout the year at $110 per month and lose only two months' benefits, whereas, under the previous law, he would lose all twelve. Individuals over the age of 72 may earn any amount without forfeiting their benefits. This is a far cry from the original law, which permitted retirees to earn only $15 per month without losing their benefit payments.

In 1956, the Social Security Law was further amended to permit permanently and totally disabled workers, who are between the ages of 50 and 65, to collect their benefits providing they meet certain requirements concerning the length and recency of covered work, and serve a six-month waiting period. In addition, the age at which women become eligible for benefits was lowered from 65 to 62 years.

Full benefits are now paid at age 62 to women eligible for benefits as widows or dependent parents. Working women and wives without child beneficiaries in their care, who elect to receive their retired worker's or wife's benefits while they are between the ages of 62 and 65, receive an actuarially reduced payment. As under the old law, the wife of a retired worker will receive full benefits regardless of age if she has a child beneficiary under her care.

Individual savings and investments.—The belief that each person should set aside, from current income, sufficient funds to provide for old age is attractive but unrealistic. Few individual workers will, even if they can, save enough during their working lives to support themselves during retirement. In 1900, when no fixed retirement age was common, workers could look forward to an average of three to four years in retirement. Today, the individual male at age 65, when he is forced to retire, has a 50–50 chance of living another 12 to 15 years. The amount of money he will require in retirement is much greater. Home ownership is one factor that aids the elderly, although it is not an unmixed blessing. Since the retirement benefits are still below income requirements, it is apparent that supplementation from savings, individual investments, or part-time employment is still needed. Most economists recommend a distribution of income between savings and investments as a hedge against inflation.[9] There is every prospect that individual savings and investments will continue to grow among increasing numbers of the population.

Old-Age Assistance.—Although approximately 2.5 million aged people are still dependent upon Old-Age Assistance programs for at least a part of their support, this form of income maintenance for the aged is gradually decreasing in importance. As shown in Figure 7, payments under Old-Age and Survivors Insurance have exceeded the Old-Age Assistance payments since 1953. Since 1950, the number of persons receiving Old-Age Assistance has remained stable at about 2.5 million, whereas the number of persons receiving Old-Age and Survivors Insurance payments has continued to rise. In June 1956, approximately one-half million individuals over the age of 65 were receiving public assistance payments as a supplement to their insurance benefits. Under the new amendments, decreasing numbers of retirees will require such supplements. Although it is improbable that the Old-Age Assistance program can ever be completely abandoned, it seems likely that it will be of diminishing importance in the total picture of economic support of the aged as time goes on.

Summary.—In summary, we can say that the general philosophy of the United States is to accept Old-Age and Survivors Insurance programs as the basis for economic support of the aged. Important advances have been made in improving the system, with respect to both the number of workers covered and the level of the payments, and no doubt other improvements will be made. It is also clear that expansion and development of private pension systems will continue to supplement Old-Age and Survivors Insurance. Employment opportunities for workers over the age of 65 will, no doubt, become more restricted, so that retirement income will become more and more important to the elderly. With the expansion of preretirement programs by industries and by labor unions, it is probable that a higher proportion of the older workers will seek voluntary retirement in the future. The support of this increasing number of individuals who have been removed from productivity will place increasing demands on our technology. If the older age group are to be maintained as consumers alone, production must be increased to keep pace with demands.

TRENDS IN | HEALTH MAINTENANCE

In many minds, chronic disease and aging are synonymous. This belief stems from the fact that physicians, social workers, nurses, and others who have to deal with many of the practical problems of older people see only those elderly who are afflicted with some disability. In their medical practice, physicians see a large percentage of older people among their patients, and hospital beds seem to be filled with them. The large numbers of elderly people who remain active in the community are not seen in doctors' offices, hospital beds, or welfare agencies. Thus, we must disassociate chronic disease from aging itself. Recent studies by the Commission on Chronic Illness show clearly that chronic disease may occur at any age.[1] Furthermore, many older persons beyond the age of 65 may be relatively healthy. For example, the National Health Survey, conducted in 1935–36, showed a gradual increase in disability and impairment with age[2] (Figure 8). In this house-to-house canvass, impairments were reported by the individual as any factor which produced some limitation in his activity, whereas disability represented impairments severe enough to make the individual homebound and unable to work. The data show an increasing incidence of impairment, so that above the age of 65, over half of the population reported some degree of impairment. However, the incidence of disability represented only about 10 percent of the population even at the age of 85. Another study, conducted on a much smaller scale in 1950, estimated that 17 percent of the 12.2 million people over the age of 65 were disabled.[3] This represents a rather marked increment from the 6.7 percent disability reported in the 55–64 age group and the 3.16 percent disabled in the 45–54 age group in the National Health Survey of 1935–36. The increasing incidence of impairment and disability with advancing age is due, in part, to the accumulative

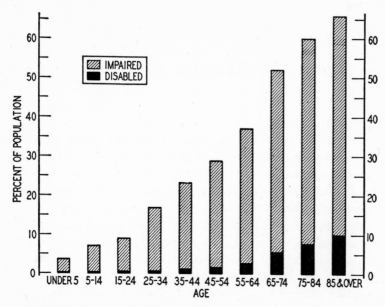

Fig. 8—Proportion of the population impaired and disabled according to age. Data from R. H. Britten, S. D. Collins, and J. S. Fitzgerald, "The National Health Survey. Some General Findings as to Disease, Accidents and Impairments in Urban Areas," *Public Health Reports, Wash.*, 55: 444, 1940.

nature of the process. Thus, a large fraction of the disability in the senescent age group arises from the progressive, but as yet nondisabling disorders that may occur some 20 years earlier. The sources of geriatric disability often start in the thirties and forties and it is among people in this age group that preventive geriatrics can be most effective. With increasing numbers of elderly people in the population, the problem of caring for these patients will increase. Obviously, our best solution is more research to discover the causes and prevention of the disabling, but nonfatal, diseases, as for example, nervous and mental diseases, rheumatism, etc. Although it may be a long time before any appreciable reduction in disease incidence will appear, progress is already being made in understanding the basic underlying causes of many of these chronic diseases.

Health status of the aged.—It is often asked whether the 65-year-old of today is in better health than the 65-year-old in 1900. This is a question for which no direct answer can be given. Although a number of surveys have been made in the past few years with regard to the general health of specific populations, and particularly the health and medical needs of people over the age of 65, the selection of the sample studied, and other technical details, make it difficult to compare studies made in different places at the same time and prevent any valid estimates of temporal trends. Various community surveys[4] indicate that many so-called healthy individuals do have symptoms of disease. Surveys for diabetes or tuberculosis, for example, when conducted in the community, always bring to light a good many unsuspected cases. The answers obtained from any survey depend, in part, on the techniques used. Surveys that depend entirely upon the verbal reports of individuals about their health status usually show a lower incidence of disease in the population than studies utilizing physical examinations and laboratory tests. When older people in New York were interviewed about their health status, about 43 percent stated that they had no physical or health problem bothering them.[5] Further questioning, focused on specific illness or physical disabilities, however, reduced this proportion to 23 percent of the sample of 500 subjects in the Kips Bay–Yorkville Health District of New York. In a small Midwestern community, 79 percent of those aged 65 and over regarded themselves as "healthy."[6] Verbal reports about health status, obtained from elderly subjects, may depend largely on the form and extensiveness of the questions asked. Thus, surveys conducted in 1955 may show a greater incidence of disease than those conducted in the 1930's, simply because methods for identifying disease have become more effective.

Deaths from cardiovascular diseases and cancer have shown a progressive increase since 1900. Thus, in 1900, only 20 percent of all deaths were attributed to diseases of the cardiovascular and renal systems, whereas, in 1950, almost 55 percent of the total deaths were attributed to this cause. In contrast, the percentage of total deaths attributed to tuberculosis showed a reduction from 11 percent in 1900 to 2.3 percent in 1950. These figures are partly a reflection of the changes in the age composition of the population since 1900 and do not necessarily mean that older individuals were more susceptible to these diseases in 1950 than they were in 1900. In 1900, a larger share of the population succumbed to childhood diseases and infectious diseases in early life, so that they did not live long enough to develop cancer or diseases of the heart and blood vessels. Thus, more people die of these latter diseases simply because more people are living to higher age categories.

It is sometimes argued that the 65-year-old person of today is apt to be more vigorous and healthy than the 65-year-old of 1900 simply because he has lived his life under circumstances of improved hygiene, diet, etc., and has therefore been exposed to less stress and strain over his lifetime. This argument is obviously based on the assumption that each disease, or the repeated insults of a lifetime, leave their mark with residual effects that cumulatively reduce the health status of an individual. Although certain inferences to this effect may be drawn from examination of mortality curves of populations,[7] we do not have specific longitudinal studies on either humans or animals that can give a direct answer to this question. All that we can say with assurance is that there are a large number of individuals beyond the age of 65 who remain relatively healthy and who are still able to perform effectively in daily living. It is certainly the hope and goal of researchers in gerontology to increase the number of such people in the future.

Special medical services for the aged.—Many middle-aged and elderly people recognize the need for specialized medical services.[8] Some physicians believe that these services can be provided best by establishing geriatrics as a branch of medical science concerned with the medical and pathological problems of older people. It is recognized that such a specialty should also include methods for maintaining health and vitality as well as the treatment of disease states in older people.[9] Since we know that many disabilities of older people stem from disease processes which may begin in middle life and continue to develop with the passage of time, it is difficult to set age limits to define geriatrics. This difficulty leads other physicians to question the desirability of establishing a new specialty at all.[10]

They believe that all of the medical problems encountered in elderly people can be adequately solved within the framework of departments of medicine and medical clinics as they now exist. These arguments are similar to those advanced in the early days of pediatrics. Experience has shown that children present problems that can be most effectively dealt with by specialists in pediatrics. Research in gerontology is only beginning to show that the aged individual is different from the middle-aged or young adult in his physiological make-up and in his reactions to disease. As we gain more knowledge from research, it will be possible to make a more rational decision about this difficult problem. However, we can say that the medical problems of aged people are apt to be extremely complex and require the highest order of medical skills for their solution.

Increasing numbers of physicians are devoting their major efforts to the care of the elderly. Many of these are members of the Gerontological Society or the American Geriatrics Society. Membership in these societies has increased almost fivefold since 1950, thus indicating rising interest among physicians in this important problem.

Advantages of early diagnosis for the effective treatment of many diseases have been widely publicized and consequently more and more people are asking for services and medical examinations even though they may have no subjective symptoms of illness. Diagnostic problems presented by middle-aged and elderly people are much more complicated than those in children and young adults because of the multiple nature of disease processes which may be present in the slow progression of the disease.[11] Furthermore, we do not know what the early symptoms of many of the so-called chronic diseases are. Availability of examination services will not only assist middle-aged and older people to maintain their health, but will also provide a great deal of needed information about the early stages of chronic disease. A number of physicians are now offering such services, but many more are needed. In a few cities, special geriatric clinics have been established. The late Dr. Malford Thewlis, of Wakefield, Rhode Island, was a pioneer in this field. One of the oldest clinics in the country is that established in 1940 by Dr. Robert T. Monroe at the Peter Bent Brigham Hospital in Boston.[12] The goal of the clinic has been to offer coordinated medical and social services to the independent, working elderly group, to aid them in retaining their independence. Following this general plan, geriatric clinics have been opened in other cities, as for example, at the Home for Aged and Infirm Hebrews and the Beth Israel Hospital in New York, and at the Brooklyn Hebrew Home and Hospital for the Aged.[13] A special demonstration project has also been established in the Kips Bay–Yorkville Health District in New York.[14]

Recent surveys show clearly that older people require more medical services than the middle-aged. In California in 1955, the number of doctor visits per 100 persons per month was 61 among patients 65 and over as compared with 48 for patients 45–64 years of age.[15] In a survey covering 72,188 patients seen by physicians on four typical days in 1953 in the state of Washington, the average annual number of visits increased from 2.5 among 20-year-old males to 7 per year in males aged 65 and over.[16] Whether special geriatric clinics are established or not, physicians will be diagnosing and treating more and more elderly people in the future.

Hospital utilization by the aged.—Although only about 8 percent of the total population is over the age of 65, in 1953, 18.2 percent of the patients in general hospitals and 21.6 percent of those in nervous and mental hospitals were over the age of 65 years.[17] In contrast, 53.3 percent of the patients in convalescent and rest homes, 53.6 percent in institutions, and 54.9 percent in chronic disease, cancer, etc., hospitals were over age 65. Furthermore, the length of stay in the hospital is apt to be longer for old patients than for young. An analysis of 20,548 discharges from general hospitals operated by the Department of Hospitals of New York in 1955 showed that only 21.1 percent of the patients under age 55 were in the hospital more than 14 days, whereas 45.9 percent of the patients aged 65–74, and 48.1 percent of those over 75 years of age were hospitalized for more than 14 days.[18] In a survey conducted in Maryland by the Commission on Chronic Illness in 1954, the distribution of long-term patients, i.e., those who have been in the hospital 30 days or more, is shown in Table 11. Thus, 34.7 percent of the patients who had been in general hospitals for 30 days or more were over the age of 65. Similarly, 81–87

TABLE 11

PERCENTAGE DISTRIBUTION BY AGE OF LONG-TERM PATIENTS
IN INSTITUTIONS IN MARYLAND, 1954*

Age in Years	Proprietary Nursing Homes	Nonprofit Nursing Homes	Homes for the Aged	Chronic Disease Hospitals	Long-Term Patients in General Hospitals†	Alms-houses
Number reported by age	1,790	409	681	765	‡	450
Percentage distribution						
Under 45	1.2	3.2	0.0	8.2	35.6	2.7
45–64	11.6	15.4	1.8	26.1	29.7	23.3
65 and over	87.2	81.4	98.2	65.6	34.7	74.0
65–74	23.4	26.4	23.5	30.3	17.0	35.1
75–84	40.3	39.1	53.7	26.0	14.0	29.1
85 and over....	23.5	15.9	21.0	9.3	3.7	9.8
Median age	78	76	80	70	‡	72

* Sources: D. W. Roberts, "Characteristics of Patients in Nursing Care Institutions," *American Journal of Public Health*, **44**: 455–66, 1954; and D. W. Roberts and D. E. Krueger, "One in 8 Is a Long-term Case," *Hospitals*, **29**: 59–62, 1955.
† Excluding special units for mental, tuberculosis, and chronic disease patients. Long-term patients were defined as those who had been in the hospitals 30 days or more at the time of census.
‡ Indicates data not available.

percent of the patients in proprietary and nonprofit nursing homes were over 65. We see that the heavy load of nursing and hospital care of the aged falls on the chronic disease hospital and the nursing home.

The role of the nursing home.—The nursing home is destined to play an increasingly important role in the care of elderly people. In 1954, there were approximately 25,000 nursing homes with 450,000 beds in the United States.[19] Only about 9,000 of these homes could be said to offer skilled nursing services, and some 9,000 of them qualified only as sheltered homes without nursing care. There is a need to improve the quality as well as the quantity of nursing homes if we are to meet the needs of the future. In contrast to 1950 when only 3 states required licensing of nursing homes, 41 states now have some licensing laws on their books. The requirements are minimal and scarcely meet specifications laid down in the recommendations made by the Committee on Aging of the National Social Welfare Assembly,[20] but they represent a forward step. The National Association of Registered Nursing Homes is also contributing to the improvement of care and facilities. Raising the standards of care in nursing homes has obviously resulted in an increase in costs. In many instances, the costs are greater than allowances made by state and local governments in budgets for Old-Age Assistance, so that oftentimes the needy aged, who require nursing home services, are unable to afford them. This poses a real problem which is apt to become more acute in the future.

Home care for the aged.—There is agreement among physicians and social workers that the aged ill should be cared for in their own homes as long as possible. Considerable success has been achieved in the development of home care programs by integrating medical services with nursing and social services.[21,22] By sending physicians to the home of the patient on a regular schedule and offering visiting nursing aid, coupled with housekeeping services, many elderly patients can be adequately cared for in their own homes or in the homes of relatives. The success of these programs depends on adequate correlation of the various services involved, but it can be done, as demonstrated, for example, in New York and Cleveland. With increasing emphasis on rehabilitation for the aged sick, home care plans will assume increasing importance.

Rehabilitation of the aged.—In view of the rising costs of hospitalization, considered efforts have been made to reduce the number of long-term and elderly patients in these beds. This has contributed, in part, to a much broader conception of rehabilitation. In this country, a primary impetus has been given by the work of Dr. H. A. Rusk,[23] Dr. M. M. Dacso, and Dr. F. D. Zeman,[24] who have been in the forefront of developing programs for elderly patients which will permit them to care for themselves or to be maintained with a minimum of nursing supervision. The attitude of futility in the treatment of aged patients is being actively combated among the medical profession, and perhaps one of the most significant developments is the production of a motion picture film showing the process of rehabilitation as carried out under the direction of Dr. F. D. Zeman at the Home for Aged and Infirm Hebrews in New York.[25] The general concept is that rehabilitation methods should be applied to all individuals to produce whatever benefits are possible, and that the former goal of returning individuals to employment is much too narrow an interpretation of rehabilitation. In England, very effective programs for rehabilitation of the elderly have been put into practice by Dr. Marjorie Warren,[26] Dr. T. H. Howell,[27] Dr. J. H. Sheldon,[28] Lord Amulree,[29] and Dr. L. Z. Cosin.[30] These programs have served as a stimulus to activities in the United States, and, at present, a number of hospitals are adding rehabilitation programs. Many patients who had previously been bedridden and unable to care for themselves are now being actively treated, with the result that they can be transferred to nursing homes with domiciliary care programs, or returned to their own homes, with benefit to themselves as individuals and to society in reducing costs of care.

In 1950, the trend was toward the construction of more hospitals for the chronically ill and the segregation of elderly patients into special hospitals. During the past five years, there has been a recognition of the major difficulties in such programs and acceptance of the concept that the chronic disease hospital is not the ultimate answer to the problem of medical care for the elderly. A wide variety of medical services are needed by aging people, and the fatalistic philosophy of providing only custodial care is no longer in step with the times. Although hospital beds will still be necessary, the chronic disease hospital of the future will serve as the focal point for aggressive medical care and rehabilitation procedures, with associated nursing homes and "halfway houses" coordinated with programs for home care. In Peoria, Illinois, an integrated program of rehabilitation and medical care, within the framework of the total community resources, has been stimulated and supported by the Forest Park Foundation. This program includes rehabilitation services for all the people in the community without specific reference to age. Hospital services as well as nursing home and home care procedures are coordinated and supervised by the Visiting Nurse Association. Of special significance is the utilization of middle-aged and older women in providing home care and housekeeping services. Similarly, the Home for Aged and Infirm Hebrews in New York maintains a number of levels of medical service. Beginning with the hospital, with an active rehabilitation program, individuals may then be transferred to a domiciliary care program, to individual apartments, or to their own homes in the community. Throughout the program, medical and social work services are provided and, where necessary, readmission to the hospital, or other aspects of the program may be provided for periods of therapy and care. It is obvious that such coordinated programs, utilizing all resources of the community, represent essential developments for the future.

Health and hospital insurance for the aged. — Although older people are more frequently ill than others in the population, they have less money to buy medical care and fewer opportunities to obtain such care on a prepaid basis. As shown in Table 12, less than half of the families with a male head, aged 65 or over, were covered by any voluntary health insurance plan. Among Old-Age and Survivors Insurance beneficiaries, 71 percent had no health insurance of any kind in 1951.[31] This is partly because enrollment methods rely heavily on group participation, usually at a place of employment. Furthermore,

TABLE 12

ESTIMATED PERCENTAGE OF FAMILIES HAVING VOLUNTARY
HEALTH INSURANCE, BY SEX AND AGE OF
HEAD OF FAMILY, 1953*

Age and Sex of Head of Family	Percent of Families in Each Group with Some Coverage	
	Male Head	Female Head
Total	66	48
65 and over	46	30
65–74	50	32
75 and over	35	27

* Source: O. W. Anderson and J. J. Feldman, *Family Medical Costs and Voluntary Health Insurance; A Nationwide Survey,* Health Information Foundation (New York, McGraw-Hill Co., 1956). The survey is based on single home interviews of 2,809 families. The families comprise 8,846 individuals representing a national "area probability" sample of the United States, subdivided by age, sex, income, size of family, rural-urban location, occupation, and region.

some prepaid plans either limit the number of older persons enrolled or exclude them altogether. Older persons are also at a disadvantage in the purchase of individually written commercial policies. Some of these policies are cancelable at the older ages, and others require such high premiums that few can afford them. In recent years, there has been an attempt to permit older employees to continue participation in health and hospital insurance plans after retirement. In addition, some associations of retired employees have negotiated plans with voluntary health insurance groups whereby their members may be accepted in a group plan.[32]

One of our most pressing problems is to devise methods for financing the costs of medical care of the elderly. One plan is to increase contributions under the Social Security Act to set up a special fund for payment of health costs after retirement. The plan envisages payment from the fund to private health insurance plans now in existence to continue insurance coverage for hospital costs after retirement and payments to private physicians, selected by the retiree, for medical services as required. It is proposed that this special fund be administered by a board consisting of representatives from medicine, government, and lay groups such as labor unions, fraternal organizations, and religious groups.[33]

Public health aspects.—It is now recognized that the maintenance of health and vigor in the aging has important public health aspects.[34,35,36] A number of states, such as Indiana, Massachusetts, New York, Connecticut, and California, have established special divisions within their health departments to deal with adult hygiene and aging. One of the first to be established, in 1945, was the Division of Adult Hygiene and Geriatrics in the Indiana State Health Department. The objectives of the Division are: (1) to study the factors of life that are related to senescence and senility as these are influenced by age, environment, heredity, and the diseases and disabilities associated with advancing years; (2) to help the public to know that senescence is normal, that senility is not a necessary part of age, and that, through better understanding and cooperation, much of the premature deterioration of aging can be prevented; (3) to have the public informed on all helpful preventive knowledge concerning diseases and disabilities of advancing years, and to encourage the medical profession, both in teaching and practice, to be interested in the problems of aging, particularly in the anticipation of preventable diseases of increasing years; (4) to cooperate with and assist, so far as possible, the public and medical profession, as well as public officials and others, in a full appreciation of the economic, social, and functional value and usefulness of men and women who, by reason of years and experience, constitute an increasingly important part of our population; and (5) to be interested in all laws and regulations and facilities which affect the care and well-being and usefulness of elderly people, and to seek the improvement of such laws, regulations, and facilities as may affect elderly people adversely.

The Bureau of State Services of the U.S. Public Health Service has established a special section to assist states and local communities to develop their own programs for the aged.

With increasing knowledge about the etiology of some of the chronic diseases, it is apparent that public education in the field of adult hygiene is of great importance in reducing the disabilities among older people. Such projects can be initiated and staffed by health departments in states and local communities, and can serve the same function among adults as well-baby clinics do for children. Although the U.S. Public Health Service stands ready to offer assistance, specific plans and programs must originate within local communities where the needs are best known.

Summary.—Although not all elderly people are ill, many are subject to varying degrees of disability. With increasing age, there is a rising need for medical and hospital care. Restricted incomes among the aged limit their ability to meet the costs of medical services. There is an increased realization that effective medical care for the aged requires the organization of all community resources to provide individualized services. There has been a broadening in the concept of rehabilitation, and many patients, previously denied the advantages of training because it was unlikely that they could be returned to the labor force, are now being treated. There is a rising demand for the establishment of health maintenance clinics for adults. With increasing knowledge about the causes of many chronic diseases, we can all look forward to a healthier old age.

TRENDS IN | **LIVING ARRANGEMENTS**

The supply of adequate housing and living facilities for older people still lags behind the demand, although a number of significant developments have taken place over the past five years.[1] The increased demand for housing of the elderly is partly a result of changes in our cultural pattern. Twenty years ago, three-generation families were common. In rural communities, parents and children continued to live with a minimum of difficulty in large houses on farms. However, a major shift from rural to urban living has taken place in the United States since 1900. As shown in Table 13, 60 percent of the total population lived on farms in 1900 as compared with only 19 percent in 1950. This trend has been even greater among the aged. In 1950, almost 86 percent of those aged 65 or over lived in cities and their suburbs, or in small towns. This shift from rural to urban living poses special problems for the aged, since cities provide a less favorable environment for them, with fewer job opportunities outside the home. Homes are smaller and there is just no place for grandpa in a three-room city apartment of today. At the same time, development of household appliances has reduced the number and burdensomeness of household chores and, consequently, the usefulness of the older relative. The trend toward smaller and more compact housing units offers little in the way of housing arrangements for parents living with married children or for three-generation families. Furthermore, the low economic status of the large bulk of elderly people limits the type of housing to which they have access.

Where the elderly live.—Although we are apt to think first of the group of elderly people maintained in various institutions throughout the country, this represents only a small proportion of the old folks. In 1950, for instance, 94 percent of persons aged 65 and over were living in households of some kind (Table 14). Seventy-seven percent

TABLE 13

URBAN-RURAL DISTRIBUTION OF THE TOTAL POPULATION
AND OF THE POPULATION 65 YEARS AND OVER
IN THE UNITED STATES*

Year	Total	Urban	Rural Nonfarm	Farm
		Total Population		
1900	100.0	39.7	†	60.3
1910	100.0	45.7	†	54.3
1920	100.0	51.2	19.1	29.7
1930	100.0	56.2	19.3	24.6
1940	100.0	56.5	20.5	22.9
1950	100.0	59.0	22.0	19.0
		Population 65 Years and Over		
1910	100.0	42.9	†	57.1
1920	100.0	47.4	24.5	28.1
1930	100.0	53.1	23.5	23.4
1940	100.0	56.2	21.8	22.0
1950	100.0	63.8	21.9	14.3

* Source: Bureau of the Census, *Sixteenth Census of the United States, Population,*
Vol. II, Part 1, Tables 1, 3, 7, 9; and *Current Population Reports—Population Character-
istics,* Series P-20, No. 26, Table 4. Bureau of the Census, *U.S. Census of Population,
1950,* Vol. II, *Characteristics of the Population,* Part 1 (Washington, D.C., Government
Printing Office, 1953).
† Not available.

of the aged males and 62 percent of the aged females were living in
homes of their own. Only 8 percent of the males and 13 percent of the
females were living with relatives other than their spouse. About
one-fifth of the group (13 percent of the men and 28 percent of the
women) were living with relatives.

Although there has been a slight increase in the number of aged
living in institutions (2.5 percent in 1900 to 3.1 percent in 1950), the
total number is still relatively small and is accounted for by the increased number in mental hospitals (0.4 percent in 1900 to 1.1 percent in 1950).[2] It is significant that the total number of elderly in

TABLE 14
HOUSEHOLD RELATIONSHIPS OF PERSONS 65 YEARS
OF AGE AND OVER, BY SEX, 1950*

Type of Household and Household Relationships	Total	Men	Women
Total	100	100	100
In households	94	94	95
Own household	69	77	62
Married and living with spouse	44	60	30
Living with relatives other than spouse	11	8	13
Living alone, or with nonrelatives	14	9	19
Not in own household	26	17	33
Living with relatives	21	13	28
Living with nonrelatives	4	4	4
In quasi-households	6	6	5
Total	100	100	100
In families (one or more relatives present)	76	80	71
Not in families (no relative present)	24	20	29

* Source: Committee on Aging, Federal Security Agency, *Fact Book on Aging* (Washington, D.C., Government Printing Office, 1952), p. 48.

institutions for the aged is decreasing (2.1 percent in 1900 to 1.8 percent in 1950), with a marked decrease in the population of public institutions (1.5 percent in 1900 to 0.5 percent in 1950). There was a slight increase in enrollment in private institutions for the aged (0.6 percent in 1900 to 1.3 percent in 1950). The major problem of housing is the provision of adequate facilities for old people to maintain themselves.

Housing aspirations of the aged.—A number of surveys have been made to find out what kind of housing the elderly actually want. Although the specific types of housing desired vary somewhat with the region of the country and the socio-economic background of the individual, one common factor is that all of the elderly people interviewed expressed the desire to live alone in their own households rather than with their children. Practically none of the interviewed groups show any inclination to choose congregate living in any form.

In Manhattan, Kansas, a survey of 50 older families revealed that their first preference was to continue living in their present homes.[3] Poor health did not alter their desire for independent living arrangements. In the event of illness, they indicated that they would want to continue in their own homes under the care of a nurse or companion. A study of retired people in St. Petersburg, Florida, indicated that both men and women wish to live in self-owned, detached dwellings.[4] The same disinterest in communal types of housing was evident in a recent survey made of housing preferences of older people in Grand Rapids, Michigan.[5]

In a survey of the aged in the state of Rhode Island, approximately one-third of the 2,400 persons, who admitted dissatisfaction with their current housing, indicated that they would like to maintain their own living quarters but still be near other old people and have access to community facilities for recreation, housekeeping, etc.[6] Most of these surveys have been concerned with older individuals who are in relatively good health. It is possible that the desires for housing among older people in poor health might show a greater preference for some type of communal or sheltered care facilities. However, the expressed preferences of older people were to have maid services and access to recreational facilities, but independence with respect to their financial and social affairs, and arrangements for their medical care.

Although limited in scope, our present knowledge indicates that no single formula is adequate to describe the housing preferences of all of our elderly. Privacy and independence, without segregation or isolation, are the qualities most commonly desired. The healthy aged want housing of an appropriate type, situated in close proximity to community services, to members of their families, and to homes of their friends. Most of them want to continue to live in their home communities, but, if they migrate, they want to live as independent families. Some of the expressed wishes of the elderly seem to be unrealistic in terms of space distribution. However, this may well be due to long-established prejudices and to the lack of knowledge among older people about the possibilities in newer housing developments.

Standards for housing.—A number of groups have been concerned with housing of the aged. A committee of the American Public Health Association has compiled a set of guiding principles for healthful housing of the aging.[7] This committee strongly urged the integration of housing for the aged within the framework of the total community and opposed the establishment of special communities for the aged. The report points out that the basic principles of good housing are applicable to all ages and that few special features are necessary for older people. These features include designs for all living space on one floor, with no stairs to climb; equipment, including shelving, of proper height to avoid bending, overreaching and climbing; adequate automatic heating devices; elimination of raised door sills; adequate lighting; nonslip floors; hand rails for bathtubs; and adequate storage space.[8] A minimum of 750 square feet is required for a two-person family. Other agencies, such as the Massachusetts State Housing Board, have also drawn up standards of design for housing the elderly, and have worked out specific plans for bathrooms, kitchens, etc.[9,10]

The Committee on Aging of the National Social Welfare Assembly has formalized standards of care for older people in institutions.[11] This report deals with special aspects of design and construction, as well as administration of homes for the aged. In 1956, this committee, in collaboration with the *Architectural Record*[12] and *Modern Hospital*, sponsored a contest for the design of housing facilities for both ill and able-bodied aged. There were over 1,200 entries from all parts of the United States and 14 other countries of the world. The first prize of $5,000 was awarded to J. J. Jordan, a Philadelphia architect, and H. Yang, advanced student in architecture at the Massachusetts Institute of Technology, for their design of a home for the aged.[13] The competition was of great value in bringing to the attention of architects the need for imagination in designing institutions with a homelike atmosphere, coupled with a high degree of flexibility.

The general trend of thinking with regard to housing takes a dim view of segregating older people into special communities or housing projects. It is believed that to provide the kind of integration of older people within the framework of community life, they should not be segregated. Thus, rather than building special housing projects for the aging, it is recommended that a number of dwelling units be made available for older people within the framework of the total housing program. This recommendation seems to be in accord with the preferences of a large share of our older people. Nevertheless, the success of special apartment dwellings, catering to the aged, in some of our large cities, such as Miami and Los Angeles, as well as the establishment of entire communities of older people by private realtors in Florida and other areas, indicates that some of our elderly prefer to live in groups of their peers rather than in mixed communities. Consequently, future developments will undoubtedly be in the direction of providing both types of living accommodations.

How older persons are housed.—Our best information about how older people are actually housed comes from a special census tabulation prepared in July 1951. This survey of one in 1,000 nonfarm dwelling units was made by the Bureau of the Census for the Division of Housing Research of the Housing and Home Finance Agency.[14] The survey showed that there were between 5 and 6 million households with the heads 65 years and over. This constituted 15.4 percent of all households in the United States, although persons 65 and over constituted only about half this number (8.2 percent). Households headed by persons over 65 tended to have larger dwelling units than those occupied by the general population. Of all nonfarm households of the nation, 51.5 percent occupied five rooms or more, while of nonfarm households headed by persons aged 65 or older, 58.1 percent had five rooms or more. The equivalent figures for dwelling units of five rooms or more were 29.6 percent for the general nonfarm population and 38.6 percent for households headed by persons 65 or older. If the commonly used standard of more than 1.5 persons per room was used to denote overcrowding, only 2.2 percent of the households headed by persons over 65 were overcrowded, as compared with 5.5 percent for the general population. The older individuals also lived in substandard units. Of all dwelling units occupied by nonfarm households headed by persons over 65, only 63.9 percent had a private toilet and bath and hot running water, and were not dilapidated. The corresponding figures for all nonfarm households in the United States was 70.4 percent. Approximately 1.2 million units occupied by those 65 and over lacked a private flush toilet or bath.

Although persons over 65 in America were home owners to a much greater extent than Americans in general, the median estimated value of these structures was substantially less than the average for the country. Thus, 69.2 percent of the male heads over 65 were home owners as compared with 53 percent in the total population. For the nation as a whole, the median estimated value of nonfarm, one-dwelling unit structures was $7,400 as compared with $6,000 for heads over 65. The study also showed that persons over 65 paid lower rents than the rest of the population.

Older individuals are more likely than the average householder to live in one- and two-person households, to be less overcrowded, and to live in dilapidated dwellings, to own their own homes, to own a higher proportion of homes of low value, and to pay less rent.

The greater longevity of females than males also has a bearing on problems of housing. As a result of the differential mortality, the ratio of females to males increases markedly in later years (Table 15). At ages 65–74, 70 percent of the males have a living spouse, but only 40 percent of the females are in this situation. At ages 75 and over, the discrepancy becomes even more marked; 49.5 percent of the males have a living spouse, whereas only 17.6 percent of the females fall into this class. Between 1947 and 1953, the percentage of married persons over age 65 increased in both sexes. Although the percentage of widowed males decreased in the group 75 and over, there was an increase in widowed females. Since the longevity of females is increasing at a more rapid rate than males, the housing of widowed females will become of increasing importance. At the present time, 40.5 percent of the single women over age 65 are living with relatives.

Privately sponsored communities for the retired.—In the past, most housing programs for the elderly have been, in part, subsidized by church groups, fraternal organizations, labor unions, and private philanthropic agencies. Recently, however, a number of programs have been established under private management. These plans range

TABLE 15

Marital Status of Persons 45 Years of Age and Over by Age and Sex, 1947 and 1953*

Sex and Marital Status	Age Group							
	45–54		55–64		65–74		75 and over	
	1947	1953	1947	1953	1947	1953	1947	1953
Men	100.0	100.0	100.0	100.0	100.0	100.0	100.0	100.0
Married	85.7	85.9	81.3	80.1	73.4	74.2	53.1	57.3
Wife present	82.5	82.4	77.9	76.5	70.4	70.0	49.5	54.7
Wife absent	3.2	3.5	3.4	3.6	3.0	4.2	3.6	2.6
Widowed	3.2	2.4	7.8	7.4	17.7	15.6	37.7	34.7
Divorced	2.0	2.7	1.9	2.8	1.3	2.1	0.8	1.0
Single	9.1	9.0	9.0	9.7	7.7	8.1	8.4	7.0
Women	100.0	100.0	100.0	100.0	100.0	100.0	100.0	100.0
Married	77.5	78.0	65.3	63.9	42.2	46.9	19.3	20.2
Husband present	73.9	73.7	62.8	61.0	40.2	44.6	17.6	18.2
Husband absent	3.6	4.3	2.5	2.9	2.0	2.4	1.7	1.9
Widowed	12.2	10.8	25.3	26.3	47.1	44.8	71.9	73.3
Divorced	2.4	4.0	1.8	1.9	1.3	1.1	0.5	0.1
Single	7.9	7.1	7.5	7.9	9.4	7.1	8.4	6.5

* Sources: 1947 data—Bureau of the Census, *Current Population Reports, Population Characteristics*. Series P-20, No. 10, Table 1. 1953 data—*ibid.*, No. 50, December 6, 1953.

from real estate developments, catering primarily to retired individuals, to apartment-hotel plans. For example, in Florida, a number of real estate promoters have planned small individual unit dwellings and have put on active campaigns to attract older people. We do not have any reliable figures on the success of these plans or on the proportion of retired to working people in these communities. Although the housing costs are somewhat less than in other parts of the country, at present it is possible for only a relatively small proportion of the elderly to take advantage of these opportunities because of costs. Although a number of cities in Florida, as for example St. Petersburg, have become centers for retired people, they cannot be regarded as primarily communities of aged. In contrast, the Florida Sun Deck Homes Company has established a group of 1,500 homes which it hopes to expand into a community of retirees. This company considers its efforts the first large-scale attempt to tackle the problem of providing housing in healthful comfort for retired people. "Leisure City," as it is called, is situated just off the Florida Keys, 24 miles south of Miami. The basic unit is a home of three rooms occupying a space 30′ x 28′ on lots varying in size from 80′ x 100′ to 100′ x 128′. Cash price for the basic unit is $5,280, which requires a down payment of $690. In order to finance the purchase, the buyer must have an income of at least $140 per month; the monthly payments, which include interest, repayment of the loan, taxes, and insurance, are $31.85.

Another retirement village, Ormond-by-the-Sea, is being built by venture capital about eight miles north of Daytona Beach. Two basic house plans are available: a one-bedroom unit for $5,250 and a two-bedroom unit costing $6,950. Two hundred forty-eight homes were already occupied in this development by 1954. There is no evidence that recreational or community activities are being developed as part of the plan.

Orange Gardens, Kissimmee, Florida, is another example of a retirement community offering specially designed individual homes at $6,000 to $9,000. Although emphasis is placed on planning for community activities, there is no evidence that the promoters of the project have considered the question of medical and hospital care for the retiree. Some retirees have chosen the trailer park for their housing.[15] While this form of housing provides mobility, it often fails to meet standards of space, sanitation, and cooking facilities regarded as desirable.

Not all of the communities for retirees are located in Florida. For example, a corporation called "Senior Estates" was organized by a group of investors in Los Angeles in 1953. The corporation bought a ghost lumber town in the state of Washington, including 400 houses, business buildings, a recreational hall, and public utilities. The exteriors of the houses were rehabilitated, but the interiors were left intact. The two-bedroom houses are being offered for sale for $2,500 each, with a down payment of $200 and monthly payments of $20, and the three-bedroom units for $3,500, with $300 down, and $30-a-month payments. The buyer must also be prepared to restore the interior of the house. Annual assured incomes between $1,620 and $3,000 are required of purchasers. Residents are encouraged to establish businesses along the lines of their previous skills, in the hope that the older people themselves can supply most of the needs of the community. Medical care is being provided in a clinic operated by a registered nurse working under the supervision of a physician who gives one day a week to the community. If this plan proves successful, it may open the door to the utilization of other abandoned properties in the United States, providing they are not too isolated.

Closely associated with the question of housing the elderly is the problem of providing adequate medical care. Where elderly individuals are incorporated into the total community, these resources may be utilized for medical care. However, where large groups of older people are congregated in special communities or in special housing facilities, community resources may be strained. This question has not been given sufficient attention in many of the real estate developments that are now being planned for older people. Although retirement benefits may be sufficient to permit purchase of individual homes, it is highly questionable whether income can also cover medical and hospital facilities when they are needed by the older person. While it is true that some of these communities have plans for special nursing and hospital facilities, the methods of staffing and financing such facilities have not been thought out. Large trailer parks for retired people exist in Florida without any specific plans for medical care. This may not be a major problem in groups between the ages of 65 and 75, but certainly, as these communities mature, the problem will become more and more acute. There is no reason why certain aspects of medical care, such as home nursing, etc., could not be provided by the able members of the community, but some specific arrangements for professional services and for hospitalization will certainly need to be worked out.

Private residential hotels.—Aged people, with above-average incomes, may also take advantage of a number of private hotels which cater to this group. In some of these, as for example in Pasadena, California, and Miami, Florida, lifetime contracts, covering not only housing but also medical and hospital care, may be purchased on admission. These contracts are relatively expensive (approximately $22,000 for a woman aged 65) and the admission fee is also relatively high ($5,000–$12,000 depending upon the facilities purchased). Individuals who do not choose to buy the life-care contract can, after payment of the admission fee, live in the hotel at a monthly rental of $160–$200 per month. These plans offer maximum freedom and privacy and, since the hotels are centrally located, meet the housing requirements for many individuals in the upper-income brackets who prefer this type of living. In a number of these programs, as for example Miami, rather extensive cultural, handicraft, and activity programs are provided by the central management of the hotel.

Cooperative plans.—Intermediate between the completely private plans and subsidized housing is a new development in the form of cooperatives. The 1950 legislative provisions for the use of public funds for cooperative housing have given some impetus to the development of projects of this nature. Many types of organization are possible, and no doubt this is an area that will see considerable expansion in the coming years. One example of this type of development is Melbourne Village, Florida. Although all homes are privately owned, the membership fee of $500 in the cooperative gives purchasers the following privileges: a warranty deed to one or more Melbourne Village lots, which must be purchased for an additional

$250 per lot, a vote at the annual membership meeting, a share of the ownership of all community property, access to the park areas, use of recreational facilities and community buildings, and the benefit of discount on products bought on a cooperative basis. By 1954, there were some 90 families living in Melbourne Village and 250 tracts of land had been sold. Most of the residents fall into the category of the older age group, although the Village was not designed specifically as a retirement community. The Village has one community center which is used for educational and cultural programs for which the residents take complete responsibility.

The Ida Culver House for retired teachers was recently built as a cooperative venture in Seattle, Washington. Rooms are purchased at approximately $3,500 and each resident pays $50 a month to cover the cost of board and other services provided in the House. On death of the owner, the room reverts to the House and is resold to another retired teacher. There are 38 residents in the House.

Claremont Manor in Los Angeles has accommodations for 200 people and is also operated on a cooperative basis. Single rooms cost $5,000 and suites $7,500. The residents also pay a life-care fee based upon their age when they enter the home, which guarantees complete care, including all medical expenses, as long as they remain residents. Facilities in the home include a main residential hall, bungalows housing 8 to 12 people, a clubhouse, an administrative building, and a chapel.

Public housing.—The United States Housing Act of 1937 limited federal aid to housing for "families of low income." Although an elderly couple would meet the requirements of this definition, local authorities have been loath to provide facilities for elderly couples because of complications arising when one partner of the marriage dies. At the insistence of the Welfare Council of New York City in 1939, the New York City Housing Authority included 50 specially designed units for single, aged persons living alone in the Fort Green Public Housing Project. These units consisted of one room of 120 square feet in floor area, with a strip kitchen along one wall, a bathroom, and a closet. Success of this project, and the increasing demands for similar facilities for old people, led the Commissioner of the New York State

Division of Housing in 1951 to issue a special order to the effect that all local housing authorities using state loan funds for public housing make a provision for the aging in all future projects. In both states, standard apartment plans have been drawn up for use in state-aided projects. [A similar provision was made by Massachusetts for housing developments using State of Massachusetts funds.] One of the units is designed for couples, and the other for single persons or remaining spouse. Both types of apartments have special adaptations to suit older people, such as the elimination of thresholds, substitution of electricity for gas in cooking, shelves placed at easy-to-reach levels, mechanical operation of windows, hand supports in the bathtubs and shower stalls, and a sunny exposure to add cheerfulness to the setting. The Chicago Housing Authority has recently authorized a 1.5-million-dollar project for housing the elderly in association with the Julia C. Lathrop project. In 1956, the Congress of the United States took special cognizance of the housing problems of older people and authorized the Commissioner of Housing to appoint a committee to explore the problem further. It is hoped that with this federal impetus, other states will move forward in accepting elderly people in their public housing facilities.

Housing sponsored by voluntary agencies.—Voluntary agencies have long been concerned with the problem of housing for the aged. Tompkins Square House in New York City, erected by the gift of a generous donor in 1929, is operated by the Community Service Society of New York on a nonprofit basis. Forty-four single rooms and eight two-room apartments for couples, sisters, brothers, or congenial persons are available. The apartments are either furnished or unfurnished as desired, with a kitchen, including full cooking and refrigeration facilities, and a bath shared with two or three others. Residence is on a month-to-month basis and rental is kept low. The cafeteria on the ground floor serves, at cost, three meals daily, except on Sunday when no supper is served. A minimum patronage is required of each resident to assure the operation of the cafeteria. A living room and lobby on the ground floor provide common rooms for residents and their friends. There is also a roof garden and a basement laundry with facilities for washing, drying, and ironing. A resident director is a registered nurse, with experience in health and welfare work, who is in charge of the House. The presence of the director gives assurance to each resident that, in the event of need because of illness or other emergency, someone is available to arrange for any action necessary. In the case of illness requiring bedside care, arrangements for hospitalization or nursing home care must be made by the resident. Though daily routine cleaning is done by the residents, a maintenance staff of the House periodically cleans all kitchens, baths, and individual rooms.

The American Women's Voluntary Services have built a row-house project of rental units in Santa Barbara, California. Fourteen individual units, located in five buildings, were built with funds collected through private donations. Each unit consists of a living room, bedroom, bath, and kitchenette of the Pullman type. Rents are maintained at a low level, and residence is restricted to people with incomes of $80 or less a month. The project is located near the shopping district in Santa Barbara. An interesting feature of this project is a community center provided by AWVS, which is open not only to residents of the housing project but to the older people of the whole community. An extensive social, recreational, and work program is carried on by a full-time director who also serves as superintendent for the housing project.

Housing subsidized by church groups.—The care of children and elderly people has been assumed traditionally by church and fraternal groups. Many religious groups have operated homes for the aged for many years. Recently, there has been a re-evaluation of the needs of older people and more attention is being paid to development of recreational and social activities.

The Jewish homes for the aged, throughout the country, have often been leaders in the development of new types of programs and services. One example of forward-looking programs may be found in the Home for Aged and Infirm Hebrews of New York. This Home, established in 1870, now claims to be the largest voluntarily supported institution for the aged in the country and is providing modern comprehensive care for nearly 1,000 older people. The central building of the Home has accommodations for 364 residents and includes an infirmary of 70 beds. It also contains a laundry, tailor shop, beauty parlor, barbershop, synagogue, library, open-air garden, occupational therapy shop, smoking and game room, and a spacious club room equipped for motion pictures, theatrical and television exhibitions. Two groups of apartments, with private accommodations for 150 men and women, are located within walking distance of the central building. The apartments contain facilities for married couples, as well as for single individuals. The residents share a common dining room and sitting rooms for recreation. The residents have a large degree of independence, but, at the same time, they can rely on the Home for medical services when needed. In addition to the apartment project, the Home operates a home care program which serves about 60 people in their own homes. Social service workers from the Home visit these aged persons regularly, and homemakers, provided by the Jewish Family Service in cooperation with the Central Bureau for Jewish Aged, help with cleaning and shopping. The medical services and the infirmary of the Home are available to those on home care when required. The nonresident members are assured accommodation in major units of the Home if they need more supervision or professional care than can be provided in their own dwellings. In 1950, Kingsbridge House was opened in the Bronx. It is operated as part of the total program of the Home. Kingsbridge House consists of six spacious interconnected modern buildings set in five landscaped areas, with special accommodations for almost 400 residents of varying degrees of incapacity. In 1950, a physical rehabilitation program was started and has achieved nation-wide recognition in successful treatment of patients who were once considered virtually hopeless. The close integration of medical, social, and psychological services is a shining example of what can be done with adequate organization.

In the past, most religious groups have usually maintained homes with a single, large, institutional-type building. New developments are in the direction of adding apartment units and detached cottages built adjacent to the large home. The National Methodist Board of Hospitals and Homes has devoted special efforts to the design and supervision of homes for the aged.[16] Emphasis has been placed on ensuring privacy for guests, with adequate programs for activities.

In addition to large national homes, such as Presbyterian Village in Detroit, the Presbyterian Church has sponsored a new decentralized plan for providing housing and care for elderly people.[17] The Presbyterian Home of Central Pennsylvania operates eight homes in five different communities. The eight homes care for approximately 130 guests. The first home was opened in Newville, Pennsylvania, in 1928. The homes are carefully selected, large residences in each community that have been acquired by purchase or gift. Each home, under the supervision of a full-time resident with some training in nursing or social work, accommodates 15 to 35 guests. All eight homes are under the general supervision of a full-time administrator. Decentralization makes it possible to offer housing and care to older people without removing them from their home communities and friends. Other advantages of decentralization include minimum capital cost for expansions in the system, low per capita cost, increased income from local communities, better coverage of the territory, and a more homelike environment. In addition, limited services such as meals and recreational activities can be offered to more older people who still live in the community. With small numbers of residents, the medical and hospital facilities of each community can be used. Decentralization of homes for the aged will, no doubt, continue on an expanded scale.

One of the major difficulties with decentralized programs of this type is the provision of medical and nursing care. However, by contractual arrangements with local physicians and hospitals, it is possible to meet these needs without the home itself actually operating nursing and hospital facilities.

Some church groups have established special communities for older people. One example is Penney Farms in Florida, which was established in the early 1930's by J. C. Penney as a memorial to his minister father and mother. The community is composed of small independent homes for the benefit of ministers, missionaries, YMCA secretaries, and other full-time Christian workers who have retired on small retirement incomes. It is located on approximately 60 acres of land and consists of some 22 cottage-type buildings of Norman-French design. There is also a large apartment building containing single apartments, a cafeteria, social room, and medical units with a resident physician. There is no admission fee, but each resident pays a monthly maintenance charge which covers the cost of upkeep of grounds, water supply, and general services.

Pilgrim Place, Claremont, California, is another village restricted to retired missionaries, ministers, and other Christian workers that is sponsored by the Congregational Church. It differs from Penney Farms in that it has been made an integral part of the city of Claremont. Pilgrim Place is situated on 28 acres of land within walking distance of the shopping center of Claremont and within easy commuting distance of eight colleges. The community consists of residence halls with small apartments for single men and women, and small homes which are usually privately owned by their residents or by Pilgrim Place. Recently an infirmary and nursing home have been built on the grounds to provide special services to the residents. With this exception, the residents utilize the total community facilities of Claremont, and regard themselves as part of the total community.

Homes for aged sponsored by fraternal organizations.—Fraternal organizations have also been concerned with housing problems of their aged members. The Masons, the Odd Fellows, the Elks, and other groups have established homes in various parts of the country. Some have followed a regional distribution of their homes, as, for example, the Masons, while others have built a single home to service their entire membership. The Loyal Order of Moose have, for example, developed an extensive colony for old people on the west bank of the St. Johns River at Orange Park, Florida.[18] The main campus of Moosehaven has an area of 68 acres, with a river frontage of over a quarter of a mile. The guests are housed in approximately ten independent cottages, each of which accommodates from 12 to 58 persons. The cottages are one-story buildings of brick veneer construction, with a central dining room, kitchen, a spacious living room, and several large screened porches in each building. A hospital unit has been constructed on the grounds and has a 25-bed capacity of private and double rooms, as well as wards, for men and women. In addition, there is a convalescent unit which accommodates 53 persons.

Medical services include a dispensary, laboratory, X-ray, and diathermy rooms. A physician and a staff of nurses provide medical and nursing services 24 hours a day. The total housing capacity of the Moosehaven community, including the hospital and convalescent home, is 374. The administrative offices and an auditorium with a seating capacity of 300 and the Moosehaven Laboratory of Gerontology occupy one large building on the grounds. Other buildings include a commissary through which all food and clothing supplies and shoe repairs are handled; an industrial shop in which are located maintenance and repair departments, and four private residences for staff members.

Recreational programs, as well as extensive programs of hobbies and other activities, play an important part in the community. A unique aspect of the program at Moosehaven is that residents participate in the operation and maintenance of the community. Jobs requiring one, two, or three hours a day are classified under more than 50 titles. Each resident draws a monthly financial allowance which depends upon the amount and type of work done and the number of hours spent each day. All those who are unable to accept job assignments because of health or other reasons are given what is termed "a sunshine allowance." Only about 40 percent of the residents are not physically able to participate in the work program. Studies have indicated that older people who accept work responsibilities are, in general, much better adjusted to their retirement than those who do not.[19]

Another unique feature of Moosehaven is the Gerontological Research Laboratory. This laboratory, established in 1950, has carried on an effective research program on the problems of aging, utilizing volunteers from the Moosehaven community.[20] A full-time research staff is supported by the Loyal Order of Moose to carry on this important work. Thus, a well-organized program, within the framework of a single community, has been developed under the sponsorship of this fraternal group.

Homes for the aged sponsored by professional groups and labor unions.—In the past, efforts of trade unions and professional groups to provide housing for their older members have resulted in the building of conventional old-age homes for printers, carpenters, actors, conductors, and soldiers. Although they have provided adequate shelter, these homes have not been notable for their development of programs. For example, the Home of the United Brotherhood of Carpenters and Jointers of America consists of one large institutional type of structure, situated in beautifully landscaped surroundings, at Lakeland, Florida. To be admitted to the Home, the applicant must be at least 65 years of age and must have been a member of the brotherhood for 35 years or more. Operating under the usual fraternalistic attitudes, all the necessities and comforts of life including clothing and tobacco are furnished to the residents.

In the past few years, labor unions are awakening to their responsibilities for preparing their members for retirement. For example, the Upholsterers International Union of North America has instituted a program of retirement preparation for all their members. In addition, they have purchased 634 acres of land in Florida and are developing a complete village for their retired workers called "Salhaven." An important aspect of the planning is that the village is also designed to serve as a vacation spot for younger workers and their families. The village will consist of 250 individual cottages of different sizes, bachelor lodges, an infirmary, a community center, craft shop, and other facilities, such as water supply plant and sewage disposal plant, neeeded to round out life in the village. This forward-looking group is, at present, hiring personnel to work out details of intake policy and to help design the activity programs as well as the medical services of the community. Eligible residents will be drawn from employees covered by the UIU Health and Welfare Fund, supported by premiums paid at the rate of 3 percent of gross wages of approximately 50,000 covered employees. Cottage residents will pay a basic $50.00 per month rental for one-bedroom cottages, covering all utilities and services, including hospitalization and medical insurance. Through the pioneering efforts of this union, other groups are giving serious consideration to similar programs.

Government-sponsored homes for the aged.—Traditionally, the almshouse has been the method used in caring for the destitute of all ages. Supported as a public charity, the almshouse, or "poor farm," has always been regarded as a last desperate resort. Fortunately, this form of care is gradually disappearing in the United States. It is true that conditions in many of these institutions have been exceedingly bad, but many improvements are being made. Passage of the Federal Social Security Act and the development of city and state programs of Old-Age Assistance have enabled many elderly people to live alone or in private boarding homes and have resulted in the tendency either toward the conversion of almshouses into an infirmary or toward the establishment of new centralized institutions to care for the ailing aged. In 1950, there were 30,416 males and 15,590 females receiving care in county and city homes and infirmaries for the aged. In contrast, 20,089 males and 45,312 females were being cared for in nonprofit private homes for the aged.[21] These figures illustrate dramatically the fact that more males than females seek admission to publicly supported homes for the aged, but females choose nonprofit private homes. In addition, the Veterans Administration operates a domiciliary care program for the aged which, on June 30, 1956, numbered 16,814 cases, plus approximately 8,739 who were cared for in state homes.[22] Although substantial numbers of individuals are still cared for by government-supported facilities, it is clear that they represent a very small proportion of the total population aged 65 and over. Many of the larger institutions have become aware of the necessity of providing programs for their guests, as well as housing and care. A number have added rehabilitation and occupational therapy services within the past few years. However, it is obvious that, as time goes on, the number of healthy older people seeking institutional care of this type will diminish appreciably. It is highly probable that these homes for the aged are ultimately destined to become nursing homes which will need to supply some medical supervision and nursing care for their guests. For the large homes already physically associated with hospitals, this will not represent a major problem. However, those homes which are maintained independently or are in isolated areas may have difficulties in making an adequate adaptation to changed circumstances.

Foster home care.—A number of social agencies in the larger cities have initiated programs of foster home care for single elderly people.[23,24,25] Patterned after the foster home placement that has proved successful with children, a social agency carefully selects both homes and clients. Minimum requirements for a suitable home include a private room, acceptable food preparation and serving in the family, the privilege of having visitors to the home, the use of the telephone, and the acceptance of supervision by the agency. The foster family is paid a fixed rate, and it is assumed they will accept the elderly client as a member of the family group. The social agency attempts to select clients that will adapt themselves to the foster family. The success of a program for foster grandparents really requires some common bond such as religion or nationality.

Summary.—From information now at hand, it is apparent that a great majority of healthy aged people prefer housing which will afford them privacy, independence, and the opportunity to remain active participants in community affairs. To meet these needs, a variety of plans have been proposed. However, the restricted income of older people indicates that the majority will require some type of low-cost housing. Many older people prefer to remain in the communities in which they have spent their working life, so that their housing becomes a community problem. Current trends in the construction of homes for the aged are definitely away from large institutions with open wards and dormitories. The keynote of housing for the aged is integration within existing communities rather than segregation.

7

TRENDS IN | **EDUCATION**

Education in gerontology has a number of facets. The first is concerned with all adults in our society and has, as its goal, the production of individuals with interests and skills to permit them to enjoy a healthy old age. Although there has been a major expansion of educational programs for retired people, it is recognized that effective programs must extend over the entire age span. In fact, we ought to be teaching some of the facts about aging within the framework of our secondary schools. It is here that changes in attitudes of our society toward older people, and the attitudes of people toward the process of aging, will come about.

The second facet of education in gerontology deals with the training of individuals to carry out programs with and for older people. This type of training extends all the way from instructions for lay volunteer workers to professional training of physicians, social workers, clinical psychologists, nurses, administrators of homes for the aged and nursing homes, etc.

The third facet of education in gerontology is to provide for the professional training of scientists who must provide the basic information about aging on which our action programs should be based. This means that aging must be presented as a challenging field for research to young scientists early in their careers.

EDUCATION FOR AGING

In the past, emphasis has been placed upon continued vocational and professional training for adults. It is now recognized that for effective adjustment of older people in retirement, we must go further and provide training in activities that will offer personal and social satisfaction. Since most of our older population must look to self-employment and self-motivating activities for their later life, more emphasis must be placed on the development of creative talents and the broadening of interests. One solution for this problem is the expansion of community colleges which all segments of the population might attend together, rather than establishing special teaching facilities for the aged. Expansion of summer session programs, with special inducements and fellowships for adult couples to spend two weeks in a college environment, might well induce significant numbers of middle-aged to reactivate and broaden their knowledge and interests.

Goals of adult education.—The primary aim of adult education programs is the development of interests, skills, and attitudes that will make possible a richer and happier life.[1] The second purpose is to impart knowledge and skills that will maintain health, retain or increase mental capacity, and enable the person to use his own resources more effectively and make the most of the facilities available in his environment. The third purpose is to offer a stimulating experience. Everyone, regardless of age, gains satisfaction from acquiring new skills. This satisfaction needs encouragement and exercise in adults and is closely related to the maintenance of an attitude of curiosity. As pointed out by the late Dr. A. J. Carlson,[2] curiosity is a characteristic which is present to a high degree in the very young, and which, unfortunately, disappears in all too many people with the attainment of maturity. Children wonder and ask many questions. Some adults and older persons preserve this attribute and see life as a series of new, interesting, and valuable experiences. The maintenance of this attitude is one of the major goals of adult education.

Learning capacity and age.—The proverb "Old dogs cannot learn new tricks" is not in accord with research findings on the learning capacity of older people.[3,4] The author of the proverb simply forgot to add that you cannot teach any dog new tricks unless he wants to learn them, and the teacher must know more than the dog. All too often, neither of these conditions is fulfilled in adult education programs. A great many studies have served to define optimum conditions for learning. However, most of them have been carried out on children and young adults, and may not be applicable to older people. We do know, however, that older people can learn under conditions of adequate motivation, even though their rate of learning may be slightly less than for children. The major problem is that of motivation. Perhaps one of our greatest needs is to make clear to adults what is known about the steps in learning. In the early stages, the learner makes errors, feels inadequate, and is ill at ease. As time passes and practice is continued, fewer errors are made, response is quicker, accuracy increases, tension disappears, and a better product results. William James pointed out that failure to recognize these steps in learning keeps many a youth from realizing his fullest possibilities. Discouragement by early mistakes is a normal stage in learning which is not peculiar to adults. Maintenance of motivation is one of the primary problems of the teacher. Because of his large backlog of experience, the older individual may suffer some disadvantage in learning new skills, since he may rely on old habits and is therefore less likely to develop new ones. Of perhaps even greater importance is the fact that the older person is more concerned about the effects of his errors as a reflection of his social status within a group. It is, therefore, important that we study, in more detail, the factors which affect learning in the adult.[5,6]

Years of schooling completed by aged.—In considering educational programs for older people, it must be remembered that more than one-fifth of those over the age of 65 have had less than five years of formal schooling, and that actually 7 percent have had none (Table 16). In 1950, half of the people aged 65 and over had received less than 8.2 years of formal education, whereas half of those aged 25-29 had received at least 12.1 years of schooling. Between 1947 and 1950, the percentage of individuals over age 65 who received less than five years of schooling fell from 21.7 to 15 percent and the percent attending at least three years of high school increased from 7.8 to 10 percent. These differences reflect the expansion of educational facilities and the increased emphasis on schooling in recent decades. It also has an important bearing on the level on which teaching and instruction must be set in order to be effective with older people.

Formal courses offered by universities.—One of the first special courses offered to assist people in making adjustments to old age was established in February 1948 by the University of Michigan Extension Service.[7] The course entitled "Aging and Living" was designed to

TABLE 16

YEARS OF SCHOOL COMPLETED, PERCENTAGE BY AGE GROUPS, 1950*

	Age Groups		
Years of School Completed	25 and Over	25 to 29	65 and Over
Median school years completed	(9.3 yrs.)	(12.1 yrs.)	(8.2 yrs.)
Total	100	100	100
None	3	1	7
Elementary school:			
Less than 5 years..........	8	4	15
5 and 6 years.............	9	5	14
7 and 8 years.............	27	15	34
High school:			
1 to 3 years..............	17	22	10
4 years	20	34	10
College:			
1 to 3 years..............	7	10	4
4 years or more..........	6	8	3
Not reported	2	2	3

* Source: Bureau of the Census, *1950 Census of Population, Preliminary Reports,* Series PC-7, No. 6.

provide specific information for immediate use in connection with current individual problems of older people, to give a philosophy of aging, and to offer some understanding of the relationship of the satisfaction of the needs of older people to the total social organization. Topics covered in the course included biological aging; psychological changes; maintenance of physical and mental health; living arrangements; creative activities; religion; social and economic security; and legal problems. The course met for two hours once a week. The first hour was devoted to a presentation of the topic by an expert from the faculty of the University of Michigan, and the second hour was devoted to questions and discussions within the group.

This course has been continued and expanded over the years, and materials have been prepared and made available to other groups interested in introducing such a course in their adult education programs. Other universities, such as Illinois,[8] Minnesota,[9] and Washington University at St. Louis,[10] have designed similar courses.

In addition to resident courses in universities, correspondence courses have also been developed. Based on an extension course, the University of Chicago since 1952 has offered a correspondence course entitled "Making the Most of Maturity" for middle-aged and older people.[11] The objectives of this course are (1) to give an understanding of what later maturity means to those who have reached that point in life, (2) to present information of the challenges which aging brings and of how men and women have faced those challenges, and (3) to provide a means for the individual registrant to make a systematic survey, under guidance, of his own situation and his community resources. The course consists of ten lessons which deal with social and personal attitudes toward aging, physical changes which occur with age, financial and employment problems, possible living arrangements in later life and their advantages, the use of leisure time, and a philosophy for later life. The study guide offers each registrant an opportunity to analyze his own experience in the light of ideas provided. The course was designed for persons with the equivalent of a high school education. One of the major accomplishments of the course is the demonstration to its students that there is no ready solution for their difficulties.

Other correspondence courses include "Aging and Preparing for Advanced Years" from the University of Illinois; "A Practical Course in Gerontology" from the University of Michigan, and "Retirement and How to Take Advantage of It" from the University of California.[12]

The role of city colleges and public schools.—Some universities, as for example Utica College of Syracuse University, and evening colleges such as Boston University, have offered free scholarships to individuals over the age of 65. In Boston, all courses in the evening division were thrown open to individuals in the community aged 65 and over. Under this plan, older students select any courses in which they can meet the prerequisites. When the plan was announced in January 1952, applicants were received from almost every state in the Union. Since the University could not assume the responsibility of finding living quarters and meeting the health needs of older persons who might come to Boston, it was necessary to limit the plan to residents of the Massachusetts area. The response, however, gives some indication of the potentialities for programs of this kind even though no special courses were established.

Utica College of Syracuse University has attempted to meet the challenge of being of service to its senior citizens in a number of ways. First, a senior citizen, defined as anyone at least 65 years of age, is not required to pay tuition for any courses taught by the college faculty. Only those who wish to work for a degree must meet the regular admission requirements. In addition, the senior citizens are urged to attend the series of lectures by well-known authorities in various fields, which are presented as part of the college program. The college has also sponsored a community guidance center which offers vocational counseling services without cost to any senior citizen who wishes to plan a new career. The college issues special senior citizen library cards which give older people access to the college library. Senior citizens have been invited to join in the weekly recorded afternoon music programs which are held at the college.

St. Petersburg Junior College has recently introduced a course in general gerontology which, although available for undergraduate credit, has attracted students aged 26–55. The course, covering the usual topics, depends on guest lecturers and utilizes the discussion method.

In a number of public school systems, the Department of Adult Education has given special attention to aging people. The Los Angeles city school system offers a 36-week program on gerontology. The goals of this program are to offer mental stimulation with new achievements and activities and new associations for elderly people. The programs are offered in evening classes in the various high schools throughout the city, and sessions are organized around the following topics: health; physiological aspects of the aging process; planning for the later years; nutrition; intellectual expansion; arts, crafts, and new skills; music appreciation, and trips of interest. An opportunity for questions and discussion is provided. One of the goals of the program is to increase the knowledge about civic activities and to enlist the participation of the older people. The gerontology office provides guest speakers for various aspects of the program. Part of the program includes discussion groups on world affairs, organized around specific countries.

The Vocational and Adult School, Madison, Wisconsin, offers a series of special courses for older people under the following titles: Geography as Related to Retirement; Health in Later Years; You and Your Aging Parents; You and Your Retired Husband, and Autobiographical Writing. In addition, the workshops of the school are made available to older persons who wish to develop their creative talents.

The New York State Department of Education has sponsored training institutes and has prepared a valuable brochure entitled "Retirement—A Second Career."

In Baltimore, Maryland, a special division of the Adult Education Department has been established to increase the participation of older people in the evening school program.

Schools are now providing two kinds of classes for senior citizens. One is exclusively designed for middle-aged and older persons, whereas the other embraces all ages but, for various reasons, attracts large numbers of elderly students. This is particularly true for classes in social sciences, language, and hobby craft.

Library-sponsored programs.—At the instigation of a worker in the Cleveland Welfare Federation, the Cleveland Public Library instituted an informal adult education program in November 1946. The objective of the "Live Long and Like It" library club, as it was called, was to keep its members actively participating citizens of the community. The project is administered by library personnel, but the programs are planned in accordance with suggestions from the members. From an original membership of 25, the club grew, over a period of six years, to a membership of over 700. The programs are cultural in nature and are not oriented specifically to problems of aging. For example, the subjects covered include current affairs, travel, natural history, astronomy, health, nutrition, music, and art. The program depends upon the showing of films in the afternoon sessions, which are followed by a question-and-discussion period. Books pertaining to the program are prominently displayed and offered on loan to participants. Other public libraries,[13] as for example in Boston; Brooklyn, New York; Chicago; Detroit; Milwaukee; Minneapolis; Oakland, California; and the Enoch Pratt Library of Baltimore, have subsequently organized programs. It is interesting to note that participants in these special programs have expressed a desire to maintain the group for older people. They seem to be happier and more at ease in sharing an educational experience with others of their own age.

Discussion groups.—With the development of Golden Age Clubs, there has been an increasing use of educational material for discussion of specific problems within these groups. Unfortunately, there has been very little source material dealing specifically with aging which has been appropriate for use in such discussion groups. The University of Chicago and the University of Michigan have pioneered in collecting and organizing material for group discussions. The Fund for Adult Education has recently prepared material specifically for discussion groups on aging.[14] The May 1954 issue of *Adult Leadership* was devoted to describing methods useful in developing discussion groups among adults.

Special projects.—Cold Spring Institute, founded and financed by Mrs. W. S. Ladd, is devoted to the proposition that retirement is not a withdrawal from active life, but rather another beginning. Located on a 160-acre estate, about 60 miles from New York City, the institute accepts, on a fee basis, a small number of residents for a period of nine months. During this time, the only specific requirements are that individuals take part in rhythmic exercises and attend a weekly lecture by some expert imported from outside. Otherwise, the 12 to 15 students are encouraged to devise their own program. Under the stimulation of the director, Ruth Andrus,[15] the students study in the institute's well-stocked library, work in its shops and greenhouses, tramp through its acres of woods, and set up a whole series of round-table discussions. The goal of the program is for each individual to discover new talents. The individuals participating in the program are often trained experts in the arts, sciences, and professions, and serve as instructors to others of the group. Men and women, aged 60 years or older, who by education, experience, or interests are capable and desirous of making constructive use of their later years and will enjoy contributing to as well as drawing from such a program, are eligible. While college training is regarded as desirable, its equivalent in experience and breadth of personal interests is acceptable for admission. Students are housed in rooms for single or double occupancy. There are available, on the premises, a large library, laboratory, dark room, studios for painting and ceramics, shops for wood and metal working, a greenhouse, and a variety of outdoor facilities for work and recreation. Participants in this program have discovered new talents ranging from language skills to writing television scripts, sculpturing, and painting. All have expressed a new and exciting point of view after graduating. As an experiment, this program has shown the potentialities of group stimulation among aging people and has demonstrated the need for planning for retirement among people with excellent educational backgrounds. Although this program is restricted to small segments of the total population, it is this group which, though small in numbers, is of great significance to society in terms of potential productivity.

Books for the laymen.—By far, the greatest proportion of older people must depend on other means to gain knowledge about aging. Most of them must turn to popular books, magazine articles, newspapers and pamphlets, or the radio and television, for information. Although there are a number of books available on aging, much remains to be done in assembling, digesting, and presenting, in readable form, the knowledge that we now possess. A few books of a popular nature are available which summarize the current status of our knowledge about the biological, physiological, or psychological characteristics of aging people. Individual chapters in the proceedings of the University of Michigan Conferences on Aging,[16] the reports of the New York State Joint Legislative Committee on Problems of the Aging,[17] and the proceedings of the University of Florida Institute of Gerontology[18] offer general summaries. Other general summaries and discussions of the psychological aspects of aging,[19] health and personal adjustment,[20] special problems of the elderly,[21] and community programs[22] have been published. The most prolific writing has been largely inspirational in character, with a minimum of attention to factual details.[23]

Newspapers and magazines.—In the past few years, there has been a marked increase in the number of articles appearing in newspapers and magazines on the subject of aging. Although most of these articles are oriented primarily toward social and economic problems of the elderly, many of them lean heavily upon research findings. These articles place major emphasis upon changes in the age structure of the population and the need for developing methods for utilizing the abilities of older people. They are doing much toward breaking down the popular conception that all elderly people are incapacitated or ill, and are focusing attention on the potentialities rather than the limitations of the aged. A number of newspapers are now carrying a daily or weekly column aimed particularly at aging people and the solution of their problems. The advertising of some of the large insurance companies has carried a good deal of factual information about aging. It is of interest that aging has even become a subject for at least one comic strip. *Mary Worth* presents a picture of graceful aging with the utilization of mature judgment and experience.

There have also been a number of popular magazines oriented primarily toward aging people. These magazines place primary emphasis upon planning for retirement among the middle-aged. Examples of such magazines are *Successful Retirement Annual*[24] and the *Journal of Lifetime Living.*[25] The latter is a monthly magazine which covers material ranging from current legislative developments to stories illustrating the solution of specific problems encountered by aged people. *Senior Citizen* is a monthly magazine published by the Senior Citizens of America,[26] which also deals with the problems of the retired. The National Association of Retired Civil Employees[27] publishes a magazine entitled *Retirement Life.* The Methodist Church[28] also publishes a magazine entitled *Mature Years.* The *Newsletter* of the Gerontological Society[29] and *Aging,* published by the Committee on Aging of the Department of Health, Education and Welfare,[30] contain information on current research developments as well as descriptions of action programs, announcements of meetings, and other information of interest to both lay and professional people working in the field of aging.

Radio and television.—Both radio and television play an important role in education. In the New York City area, a special program entitled "Life Begins at Eighty" has been successfully produced. Elderly people with particular accomplishments are interviewed on this program. An increasing number of programs have been devoted to various aspects of aging. "Fear Begins at Forty" was a full one-hour program emphasizing the problems of aging from the point of view of employment. In the Chicago area, a commercially sponsored program entitled "It's Your Life" has presented interviews with older people, serving to point out their problems and to offer suggestions for their solution. Discussions of the social and economic problems of aging have appeared on a number of national radio programs such as "Town Meeting of the Air" and the "American Forum." The Extension Service of the University of Michigan, with the assistance of the Institute for Human Adjustment, has prepared a series of recordings for distribution to radio stations and to communities and organizations interested in learning more about the problems of aging. In these recordings, the importance of older people to the society and the philosophy of aging are explained. The problems of personal adjustment and the methods found successful by older persons in solving them are presented in actual interviews. Some of the subjects considered in the different broadcasts are preparation for retirement, employment, mental health, religion, social security, housing, arts and crafts, citizenship, and participation in community life. The Pennsylvania State College has recorded the development of an old-age center in Syracuse, New York, in its series "The People Act." Television programs emphasizing the positive aspects of aging have also been produced, as, for example, "Such a Busy Day Tomorrow." This program was recorded and is available for group showing. "Years of Usefulness" (YOU) was presented over WRC in Washington, D.C., under the sponsorship of the Department of Public Health. The program utilized guests for interviews as well as film for presentation of eight programs covering the usual topics. The New York State University has sponsored a television educational program.

Exhibits.—In some communities, as for example Cleveland and Philadelphia, special exhibits on aging have been prepared. In Baltimore, the Museum of Art, in cooperation with the Baltimore Medical Society and the Medical and Chirurgical Faculty of the State of Maryland, assembled an exhibit entitled "Man and His Years." The exhibit contrasted paintings by famous artists made in the early stages of their careers with those produced later. Special emphasis was placed on the productivity of artists who had reached advanced ages. Artists who began painting later in life, such as Moses, Blustein, and Blair, were special features of the exhibit. The aim of the exhibit was to illustrate the latent capacities for achievement present in the aged. The Peale Museum in Baltimore also assembled a mobile exhibit on various aspects of aging which was shown in a large number of schools in the area.

Motion pictures.—In the past few years, a number of special motion pictures, dealing with the problems of aging, have been prepared. A mental health documentary film entitled *Our Senior Citizens* was prepared by the New York Mayor's Advisory Committee for the Aged and dealt with activities in a day center program for older people. *A Place to Live,* produced by Dynamic Films under the sponsorship of the Committee on Aging of the National Social Welfare Assembly,[31] offers a dramatic presentation of the problems of the three-generation family and the advantages of congregate living in a home for the aged which meets acceptable qualitative standards of sheltered care. *Adventure in Maturity* was a film produced by the Oklahoma State Department of Health, which suggests different ways in which older people can make the adjustments to retired life. The National Film Board of Canada has produced a film entitled *Date of Birth,* which emphasizes the high degree of dependability and productivity of older workers and stresses the importance of giving them a fair chance. Mental health problems are dealt with in a film entitled *Steps of Age,* which was produced by the South Carolina State Board of Health and the Mental Health Film Board, with the cooperation of the National Institute of Mental Health, Department of Health, Education and Welfare. Films have also been made dealing primarily with medical aspects of aging, as, for example, *Still Going*

Places by Dr. F. D. Zeman of the Home for Aged and Infirm Hebrews of New York.[32] This film presents, in a dynamic fashion, the rehabilitation of an elderly hemiplegic. Although this film is designed primarily for physicians and health personnel, it demonstrates the practical ways in which chronically ill or acutely disabled patients of advanced years can be helped to live useful, self-sufficient lives. The film has educational value for professional workers engaged in any program of care, as well as for the individual patient and his family. Also in the medical area is a film released by the William S. Merrell Company entitled *Problems of the Mind in Later Life*.

Preparation for retirement.—Both labor unions and management are showing increased recognition of their responsibility to aid workers in making adequate adjustments to retirement. At its recent biennial conference, the International United Auto Workers adopted a plan for meeting the needs of its older and retired workers. Preparation for retirement has been included as one of the benefits to be sought in future collective bargaining. Some labor unions have specific programs in operation. For example, the Upholsterers Union is setting up special programs in preparation for its members who are approaching retirement. Although it is recognized that preparation for retirement is a lifelong process, experience has shown that individuals below the age of 60 are not as apt to participate in special training programs as are those above 60. Nevertheless, many industries, some of them in cooperation with labor unions, are setting up special preretirement programs. These programs range all the way from the preparation of leaflets, which are distributed to the workers, to specific lectures and discussion groups that devote themselves to problems of income maintenance, health, recreation, and utilization of skills after retirement. The University of Michigan Institute of Gerontology has been a pioneer in the preparation of materials and in the operation of programs of this kind. Institutes of industrial relations in a number of universities, such as Chicago, California, and Wisconsin, have prepared material for use in preretirement programs in industry. Companies such as Esso Standard Oil, Swift Company, and John B. Stetson Company have organized specific discussion groups among their workers. The major emphasis in these programs is on offering information about retirement to the workers, and on stimulating the development of outside interests and activities which will provide an outlet after retirement. Although most companies have organized their retirement counseling programs within the framework of their own personnel department, the Retirement Council of New York[33] is now offering this service on a fee basis to industries who wish to have such services for their employees. Although individual cases can be cited where preretirement programs have been helpful, no careful evaluation has, as yet, been made. However, with the increasing number of individuals who are faced with forced retirement because of age, the need for programs of this type will greatly increase in the future.[34] Studies on the effectiveness of various techniques certainly need to be made.

As indicated in the chapter on employment, special counseling and training services for older people are effective in placing them in paid employment. This is obviously one form of education which is sadly in need of extension and development.

TRAINING LEADERS FOR ACTION PROGRAMS

Education for lay workers.—With the rising demand for action programs in communities throughout the United States, leadership has been largely in the hands of nonprofessional people who have an interest in community service. Information and guidance for this group have stemmed largely from institutes and conferences. The pattern for these conferences was based on local institutes held in New York, New England, and other communities, but was developed on a national scale by the University of Michigan, under the leadership of Dr. Wilma T. Donahue. The Charles A. Fisher Memorial Institute on Aging, held annually each summer since 1948, is addressed to two groups of people: (1) professional workers, such as adult education leaders, welfare workers, ministers, recreation workers, personnel workers, and public health nurses, (2) middle-aged and older people who wish practical information to aid them in enjoying their later years. The response to these institutes has been phenomenal. The first institute attracted a registered attendance of 132 persons divided about equally between the professional and nonprofessional groups.

The topics covered included living arrangements, rehabilitation, employment, health, and the planning of action programs, recreation, income maintenance, etc. The institute held in 1956 attracted some 1,200 persons. Following this general pattern, similar institutes have been organized in almost every state of the Union. Some of them, such as those sponsored by the Institute of Gerontology at the University of Florida, the Institute of Gerontology at the University of Iowa, and the Committee on Aging of the National Social Welfare Assembly, have met on an annual basis. Others have been organized by workers in individual communities, some on a regional basis, others on a state-wide basis, and still others on a local basis.

In response to popular demand, a National Conference on Aging was held in Washington, D.C., August 13–15, 1950, under the auspices of the Federal Security Agency, now the Department of Health, Education and Welfare.[35] The objectives of this conference were to stimulate the exchange of ideas among persons of varied experience, with the aim of meeting the problems of aging through private and public organizations in each state, city, and community; to define the nature and extent of these problems; and to promote research on aging in such fields as employment, health, education, recreation, rehabilitation, and social and psychological adjustments. One of the results of this conference was the formation of commissions on aging in many states. As part of the program of these commissions, many state and regional conferences, patterned somewhat after the National Conference, have been held. These conferences offer stimulation to local groups and serve to define the problems more clearly. In addition, the interchange of ideas among workers has proved of value in forwarding action programs throughout the United States.

A number of universities, such as the University of Chicago, the University of Illinois, New York University, Cornell University, and Syracuse University, have organized special summer institutes, or workshops, devoted to providing information to professional and lay workers who wish to organize effective programs in their own communities. There is no question but that the future will see expansion in training programs of this kind, which are somewhat more informal than the training in professional schools.

TRAINING FOR PROFESSIONAL AND RESEARCH WORKERS

Professional training in gerontology. — Gerontology has not yet come of age with respect to professional education. Professional training falls into two categories. The first is concerned with the training of professional workers such as physicians, social workers, nurses, and recreation leaders who deal with the problems of older people at the operating level. The second is concerned with providing competent scientists for research on various aspects of aging. Whatever success we may have in the solution of practical problems must rest on our basic knowledge of the physiological, biochemical, psychological, sociological, and medical aspects of the problem. In other words, for effective practical work, we must not lose sight of the necessity for training competent research workers who will continuously add to our store of knowledge. We must take steps to see that there is a continuous flow of young workers into research on aging in all its various aspects. Because of the large number of scientific disciplines which have an important bearing on aging research, no general statements about the training of these workers can be made, except to emphasize the necessity for adequate training in whatever discipline the individual chooses to work. Therefore, training in gerontology, or geriatrics, must be superimposed upon adequate training in some scientific discipline or medicine. Our major problem is not so much to ensure adequate training in these disciplines as it is to make young physiologists, biochemists, psychologists, etc., aware of the importance of problems of aging and to indicate the application of their specialty to these problems. However, since specific instruction in the problems of aging is not offered within the training programs of graduate students, it seems desirable that some of these problems be incorporated into discussions in courses at even the undergraduate level.

In the summer of 1956, the subcommittee for Social Science Research of the Gerontological Society sponsored a working conference which considered the problem of training in the social science aspects of gerontology. Representatives from a number of universities and research centers worked out, in detail, a program of training. As a result of this conference, a cooperative project involving eight different universities has received a grant from the National Institutes of

Health to assemble training materials and to work out programs on a trial basis. Dr. Wilma T. Donahue of the University of Michigan is serving as coordinator of the project.

University courses. — Surveys of university catalogues show that there are very few universities offering specific courses in gerontology. Most of these, as, for example, the New York University School of Education, the Merrill-Palmer School (Detroit), the University of Michigan, the University of Chicago, the University of Minnesota, the University of Texas, and the University of Illinois, offer specific courses in psychology and the social sciences. In the biological sciences, aging is dealt with only incidentally within the framework of other courses in anatomy, physiology, biochemistry, etc. Even at the graduate school level, specific courses in aging are conspicuous by their absence. Graduate courses are offered in the psychological or social aspects of aging at Columbia University, the University of California, the University of Michigan, the University of Minnesota, Syracuse University, the University of Chicago, the State University of Iowa,[36] and Ohio State University. Since aging is touched upon incidentally within the framework of a variety of courses, it is little wonder that the student fails to recognize gerontology as a challenging field for either professional or research work.

Medical training. — Although about one-third of our medical schools take cognizance of the problems of aging by including in their course descriptions some reference to aging, senility, geriatrics, gerontology, etc., only a handful offer specific courses. Dr. Fred D. Zeman of the Home for Aged and Infirm Hebrews of New York has been a pioneer in offering special courses to medical students and nurses[37] at the postgraduate level. Dr. Joseph T. Freeman offers a special course in geriatrics at Women's Medical College in Pennsylvania to give future physicians an understanding of the medical problems unique in old people. The University of Texas Medical Branch and the University of Kansas Medical School also offer individual courses. Courses in psychiatry, internal medicine, clinical medicine, pathology, and physiology are often mentioned as covering some aspects of aging. Only one medical school, the University of Kansas Medical School, has a department of gerontology which is part of the department of medicine. Internships and residencies in geriatrics are offered by only a few hospitals in the entire United States.

Postgraduate training in the medical aspects of gerontology has undergone a significant expansion over the past five years. In 1955, the New York Academy of Medicine devoted its Graduate Fortnight lecture series to problems of aging. This program was broadly conceived and covered all aspects of aging ranging from biology to sociology.[38] The American College of Physicians also sponsored a postgraduate course on stress and aging at the Lankenau Hospital in Philadelphia in 1955. In May 1956, the Galesburg, Illinois, State Research Hospital sponsored a conference on research in aging.[39] For the past several years, Dr. Edward H. Hashinger of the University of Kansas Medical School, Kansas City, Kansas, has offered a three-day postgraduate course in geriatrics to physicians in the Kansas City area. A number of pharmaceutical houses have also sponsored postgraduate seminars on the problems of geriatrics. For the past several years, the American Geriatrics Society has held a two-day postgraduate course on geriatrics in New York City. These programs have done much to bring before physicians our specialized knowledge about the care and treatment of older people.

Professional training in social work and administration.[40]—Schools of social work in the United States have been slow to admit the need for special training for work with the aged, and specific programs are still in the formative stages. Committees of the Council of Social Work Education and of the American Public Welfare Association are in the process of studying the curriculums of schools of social work to determine the desirability of specialization within schools. As is true of other professional groups, two alternatives for training are under consideration. According to some, training in gerontology should be organized around specific courses. Others believe that problems of the aged should be considered within the framework of existing programs in case work, group work, and community organization. One of the undecided issues is the extent to which methods and approaches in social work need to be altered because of special qualities of older people. Some schools, such as the New York School of Social Work, have developed special projects whereby students receive experience in working with older people in actual operating programs such as the Hodson Center in New York. Experience has shown that community programs for the aged can be improved by association with professionally trained social workers. Perhaps the most significant development in social work has been the recognition that many of the services for the aged can be handled best in the individual's home rather than in institutions. Older people are recognized as individuals, rather than simply as members of a group. Social workers, like visiting nurses, are beginning to go into the homes of the elderly.

In the United States, training programs for administrators of homes for the aged have been conducted chiefly on an in-service basis by various welfare groups or in conferences. In 1956, Dr. Leonard Breen of the University of Chicago conducted a course for administrators of homes for the aged. New York University is organizing a similar course in cooperation with the Community Council of Greater New York. In Sweden, about 30 directors of homes for old people have been trained each year since 1908. The Swedish Social Welfare Association has sponsored the program.[41] The training course requires three years and includes theoretical courses as well as practical experience in homes for old people, a general hospital, and a mental hospital.

Professional societies.—Recognizing that the problems of aging require for their solution an interdisciplinary approach, the Gerontological Society was organized in 1945 with an original membership of 80. The purposes of the society are to promote the scientific study of aging in order to advance public health and mental hygiene, the science and art of medicine, and the cure of disease; to foster the growth and diffusion of knowledge relating to problems of aging and of the sciences contributing to their understanding; and to afford a common meeting ground for representatives of the various scientific fields interested in such problems and for those responsible for the care and treatment of the aged. By 1950, the society had grown in membership to over 300, and in 1956 the membership reached a total of 1,200. Physicians, physiologists, biochemists, anatomists, pathologists, psychologists, sociologists, nurses, social workers, economists, etc., are all numbered among these members. Annual meetings for the presentation of scientific papers and for discussion of an interdisciplinary approach to problems of the aged have been held since 1948. In 1946, the society established the *Journal of Gerontology*,[42] which is devoted to the publication of original manuscripts dealing with the problems of aging in the fields of natural and social sciences and the humanities. In 1952, the society also established a *Newsletter* to offer information about current developments in gerontology, to describe action programs, to review books, and to offer other pertinent information.

The American Geriatrics Society was established by members of the medical profession.[43] It is concerned primarily with the treatment and prevention of diseases in elderly people. Fellowship in this society is limited to members of the medical profession. Of a membership of 206 fellows in 1950, this society has grown to a total membership of several thousand. The society also publishes its own medical journal entitled the *Journal of the American Geriatrics Society*.

In 1956, the American Medical Association established a Committee on Geriatrics of the Council on Medical Service. Under the chairmanship of Dr. H. B. Mulholland, the committee has held a number of meetings and recently altered its name to the Committee on Aging in recognition of the multiple aspects of the problem. The purpose of the committee is to explore the general field of aging, as well as its scope and problems, in order to assist medical societies and individual physicians in assuming their responsibilities toward "senior citizens" and to seek ways and means of meeting the challenge to medicine.

In 1946, the American Psychological Association organized a Division on Maturity and Old Age.[44] There are approximately 250 members of this division. In addition to the presentation of scientific papers, symposia for the discussion of pertinent problems on the psychological aspects of aging and methodological approaches to these problems have been held at annual meetings of the division. The division also stimulated the formation of a special committee of the American Psychological Association to deal with the problems of continued employment among retired psychologists.[45]

The National Geriatrics Society is an organization of institutions (old-age homes, nursing homes, sanitariums, etc.) which provide care for the aged. Incorporated in 1952, the society now numbers about 200 institutions. The aims of the society include the promotion of a code of ethics to regulate and evaluate the standards of institutions caring for the aged. It also makes available to physicians, hospitals, and the public a registry of institutions caring for the aged which meet standards set by the organization.

The First International Congress of Gerontological Societies, under the leadership of Professor L. Brull, was held in July 1950 in Liége, Belgium. Representatives of 12 European countries, Canada, and the United States attended the three-day meeting and presented scientific reports.[46] The Second International Congress met in St. Louis in September 1951, under the presidency of Dr. E. V. Cowdry. Forty-four countries from all parts of the world were represented at the five-day conference.[47] The Third International Congress was held in July 1954 in London, with representatives from 37 countries attending the five-day meeting.[48] This congress was held under the presidency of Dr. J. H. Sheldon. The Fourth International Congress was held in Merano and Venice, Italy, in July 1957, under the presidency of Dr. E. Greppi. Seven hundred delegates from 30 countries attended. The international meetings illustrate the world-wide character of gerontological research, and they have offered opportunity for the exchange of ideas for action programs and for investigations in the basic sciences. Aging knows no boundaries.

An International Symposium on Experimental Research on Aging was held in Basel, Switzerland, in April 1956 under the leadership of Dr. F. Verzár.[49]

In September 1956, the First Pan-American Congress of Gerontology was held in Mexico City.[50] This congress attracted some 300 individuals as representatives from almost all of the countries of Latin America, the United States, and Canada. Most of the countries of Europe, the United States, and a few South American countries now have gerontological societies which hold annual meetings for the presentation of papers and discussion of programs.

Special professional journals.—In 1950, there were only four professional journals in the field of gerontology. The oldest is *Zeitschrift für Altersforschung,* published in Germany. The *Journal of Geron-*

tology and *Geriatrics*[51] represented the two primary publications in the United States. In 1953, the American Geriatrics Society established its own journal, the *Journal of the American Geriatrics Society*. The past five years have seen the establishment of a large number of journals devoted to various aspects of gerontology in other countries of the world.[52] At present, there are four journals published in the United States, four in Italy, two in Switzerland, two in Japan, and one each in Argentina, Finland, Mexico, and Germany. The establishment of these journals is a reflection of the increased interest in the problems of aging. With increasing research productivity in gerontology, it is fervently hoped that the content of many of these journals will improve in quality as well as in quantity.

Scientific conferences.—The oldest conference group on problems of aging was that sponsored by the Josiah Macy, Jr. Foundation. The first conference was arranged in 1938 by Dr. E. V. Cowdry in order to give the authors of the various chapters in his book *Problems of Aging* an opportunity to meet and discuss the material. This group met annually until its termination with the fifteenth conference in 1953. Transactions of the tenth (1948) to the fifteenth (1953) conferences have been published and offer documentary evidence of the evolution in thinking with regard to research on aging over this period of time.[53] This series of conferences set the pattern and emphasized the value of informal discussions among scientists representing a wide array of disciplines. Over the past years, other scientific societies, such as the American Physiological Society in 1956[54] and the Association for Research in Nervous and Mental Disease in 1955,[55] as well as other professional societies, such as the National Council on Social Work, have devoted parts of their annual programs to symposia and discussions on problems of aging. In May 1957, the American Institute of Biological Sciences sponsored a two-day conference on biological problems of aging. Conferences have also been sponsored by the Atomic Energy Commission to discuss the long-term effects of radiation on longevity. The Ciba Foundation has instituted a series of colloquia on problems of aging; the first, held in London in 1954, was concerned with the general aspects of aging;[56] the second, in 1955,[57] considered aging in transient tissues; and the third, in 1956,[58] was devoted to methods of assessing aging. These conferences have been of great value in permitting research workers from various countries of the world to discuss informally their research programs. The groups are kept small, and, since the participants live at the Ciba House, there is a real opportunity for the development of mutual understanding. In addition, the Ciba Foundation established, in 1954, an award for outstanding research in gerontology. These conferences show an increasing awareness, among scientists of many disciplines, of the problems of aging, which offers promise for the future.

Summary.—Education is our most effective device for altering attitudes. If we are ever to eliminate the idea that aging means uselessness and accumulated disease, we must begin at the elementary and high school level to teach children something about the aging process. We must instill in everyone the idea that education is a lifelong process. Learning, in itself, can be a stimulating activity. The retention of the attitude of curiosity and of the desire to achieve new skills and new experiences is one of our most effective means of avoiding the feelings of boredom and uselessness in old age. We are beginning to see, in newspapers, radio, and television, a rejection of the idea that older people have no useful function in our society. This is all to the good, but we must encourage a more positive stand on the necessity for utilizing the capacities of older people in our society. This is a long-term educational program in which we have just begun to take the first steps, but it is only by such means that we shall ever be able to alter our outmoded attitudes and customs.

There is a rising demand for information about aging and, particularly, for training of lay people to administer action programs effectively. This demand is being met largely through summer institutes and short-course training programs. Although we have made forward steps in the professional training, much remains to be done. The increased membership in professional societies concerned with problems of aging indicates a rising interest which will undoubtedly continue at an ever-increasing pace.

COMMUNITY PROGRAMS AND SOCIAL WORK

The First National Conference on Aging, held in Washington, D.C., in August 1950, under the sponsorship of the Federal Security Agency, focused national attention on the proposition that aging has become a community problem.[1] This conference, carefully organized as an exploratory forum, considered the entire field of gerontology, ranging from population changes and income maintenance to training of professional personnel for both action programs and research. The 816 participants, from all parts of the country, were able to discuss their problems in the light of factual material which had been prepared by various working committees prior to the conference. These committees profited greatly from the experience of workers in the field of aging, as, for example, Miss Ollie A. Randall, who had been influential in organizing the Division on Welfare of the Aged, under the Welfare Council of New York City as early as 1926. Although a number of cities, such as Chicago, Cleveland, Detroit, Syracuse, San Francisco, and San Diego, had already conducted surveys to determine the needs of elderly people in their communities and the services available to meet them, this conference brought all of these workers together and made it possible to focus national attention on their problems.

State commissions on aging.—The New York State Joint Legislative Committee on Problems of the Aging has been in existence since 1947. By September 1952, some 14 states had formed state commissions on aging. In view of this development, a conference was called of representatives of these state commissions in Washington under the auspices of the Federal Security Agency.[2] This conference served to point up the problems of state organization and offered further stimulus to action by the individual states so that, by January 1957, over half of the states had established some form of advisory council, or state commissions, concerned with the problems of aging.[3] The form of the organization differs among states. In 11 states, Colorado, Connecticut, Maine, Michigan, Minnesota, New Jersey, North Carolina, Oregon, Rhode Island, Vermont, and West Virginia, temporary commissions, set up either by legislative enactment or by directive of the governor, have made special studies of the problems of aging.[4] Membership on the commissions generally has consisted of state legislators, administrative officials, and private citizens. At least in 6 states, California,[5] Colorado, Minnesota, New York,[6] North Carolina, and Washington,[7] the governor called state-wide conferences on aging. In some instances, specially appointed groups did extensive planning and staff work. In all instances, these conferences adopted resolutions for action. In 11 states, California, Colorado, Florida, Illinois, Indiana, Massachusetts, Michigan, New Mexico, New York, Rhode Island, and Washington, special advisory coordinating committees have been established on a continuing basis. Their membership includes private citizens, administrative officials, and sometimes legislators. The primary function of these committees is to suggest means for coordinating current activities in the field of aging and to stimulate the undertaking of new programs. In other states, such as New York, Kansas, New Hampshire, Ohio, Pennsylvania, and Wisconsin, legislative councils, or committees, have made broad investigations of the problems involved. The New York State Joint Legislative Committee on Problems of the Aging, established in 1947, has given broad leadership in the developing of legislative programs. Recently, the governor of New York and the governor of Minnesota have each appointed a special assistant on problems of aging who is charged with leading and coordinating departmental activities in this field. In California and New York, interdepartmental committees, composed of departmental representatives, are coordinating state programs and are giving state-wide leadership. The Connecticut Commission on the Care and Treatment of the Chronically Ill, Aged, and Infirm is the only state-supported operating agency. It directly manages institutions for the chronically ill, the aged, and the infirm. In many states, special administrative personnel, or divisions, have been designated to work with the aged. In some states, such as Indiana and Kansas, the State

Department of Health has established special divisions for geriatric problems. In Illinois, Minnesota, and Colorado, special attention has been given to problems of the aged in the State Department of Welfare. In some states, appointments to the commissions on aging have been made by the legislature; in others, this has been the responsibility of the governor. Although some states have made direct appropriations for the operation of the commission, permitting paid staffs, this is not true in all cases. With the exception of New York State, which allocated an appropriation of $25,000 per year, the budgets are relatively low ($2,000–$15,000). In general, states are not establishing special agencies, or divisions of regular departments, to deal with aging problems, but are adding this function to the duties of existing personnel. In only a few instances have special divisions, or advisers, been appointed.[8] Action programs are regarded as primarily a function of local communities. The role of the state governments has been to stimulate development of these local programs. The report of the Council of State Governments has served a useful function in bringing to the attention of the governors of all states the need for action and the progress made in the various individual states.

Federal Council on Aging.—Early in 1956, President Eisenhower established a Federal Council on Aging. Its function, according to the President's statement, is to review existing programs in the government in the light of emerging needs, and to make recommendations to the appropriate departments and agencies as to priorities and provisions for unmet needs. In establishing the council, the President said, "In considering the changed circumstances presented by the length in life span, we must recognize older persons as individuals— not as a class, and their wide differences in needs, desires, and capacities. A great majority of older persons are capable of continuing their self-sufficiency and usefulness to the community if given the opportunity. Our task is to help in ensuring that these opportunities are provided." The President listed the following areas in which emphasis for improvement should be placed: preservation of physical and mental health, and rehabilitation, income maintenance, employment and retirement, housing, living arrangements and family relationships, education, civil participation, and recreation. Membership in the council includes individuals designated by the Secretaries of the Departments of Health, Education and Welfare, Labor, Commerce, Interior, Agriculture, and Treasury; the Housing and Home Finance administrator, the administrator of Veterans Affairs, the chairman of the U.S. Civil Service Commission, the director of the Office of Defense Mobilization, the director of the National Science Foundation, and the administrator of Small Business Administration.[9] The first project undertaken by the council was the cosponsorship, with the Council of State Governments, of the Federal and State Conference on Aging, which was held in Washington in early June 1956. This conference was attended by 107 representatives appointed by the governors of 41 states, as well as by representatives from government agencies who are members of the Federal Council on Aging and of national voluntary agencies.[10] It was a working conference whose 240 participants considered problems of authorization, organization, financing, and functions of official state committees, and commissions on aging; problems of housing and family relationships, employment, vocational rehabilitation, retirement, income maintenance, education, recreation, and the maintenance of physical and mental health. Through the exchange of information and ideas, the development of sound programs will be implemented. In his closing remarks, M. D. Folsom, Secretary of the Department of Health, Education and Welfare, said, "Moreover our programs should not serve to set older people aside as a special segment or class of the population. Our programs should be designed to enable older persons to live as integrated and useful members of the family, community, and national life. Few older people want others to assume responsibilities that are rightfully theirs. Activities in the interests of older persons will render the greater service if they do not foster dependence, but instead enlarge opportunities for individual effort and encourage self-reliance, initiative, and creative endeavor. In carrying forward activities to accomplish all these objectives, no one activity can stand alone. Coordination of many activities, and cooperation by many groups, will be needed. President Eisenhower established the Federal Council on Aging not only to coordinate the programs of the various Federal departments and agencies, but also to make the resources of the Federal government more readily available to all state and local groups." We can see a pattern evolving with the development of action programs which place major emphasis on integrated activities to be initiated and carried out by local communities, with the support of the state and national governments. This means that each local community will have to decide for itself the appropriate distribution of its resources between the needs for schools, children, and the aging segment of its population. At the present time, only a small proportion of the resources of most communities are devoted to the aged and aging. With increasing numbers of older people, and the rising awareness of their needs, the time may come, in the not-too-distant future, when communities will have to decide on what proportion of their resources they are willing to devote to the aged. It, therefore, is of great importance that we utilize older people to the full extent of their capacities to provide services in the community not only for themselves but for others as well.

Recreational and activity programs for the elderly.—The past five years have seen a remarkable growth in the formation of old-age clubs and recreational centers. In some of the larger cities in the United States, full-time recreational centers that are open throughout the day, five days a week, have been established for older people. One of the first was the Hodson Center in New York City.[11] This center, opened in September 1943, offers opportunities for older people to get together for social activities of many kinds. Programs have been added according to the desires of the group, and include such diverse activities as writing, painting, woodworking, embroidery, choral singing, and dramatics. The number of elderly people served by this center has gradually increased over the years until, at present, there are over 1,000 who attend functions in the center. A similar program was established in 1949 at the Sirovitch Day Center in New York. Originally sponsored entirely by private donors, these centers are now jointly sponsored by voluntary agencies and the Department of Welfare of the City of New York, which has, over the years, helped to open additional centers throughout the city. As of January 1957, there were 60 clubs serving approximately 7,000 aged in New York. In addition, there were 17 day centers for the elderly, which had some 6,000 enrolled members. A substantial number of elderly people make use of these facilities, and some of them participate in both programs. The day center program, under the direction of a full-time paid supervisor, is spreading to other cities under the sponsorship of welfare, recreation, or adult education departments.

Another type of organization depends on the formation of recreational centers which provide weekly or monthly meetings for older age groups under the sponsorship of churches, YMCA's, community clubs, etc. One of the pioneers in this type of organization is Miss G. E. Bowen of Philadelphia.[12] The activities of the centers range from bingo games to handicrafts such as sewing, weaving, and carpenter work. The major goal of these programs is to offer social contacts and the opportunity for older people to participate in group activity. Although general supervision has been carried out by a professionally trained person, the day-to-day operation of these centers is largely in the hands of lay people.

As early as 1916, the Community Service Society of New York sponsored summer vacations for elderly people. There has been a gradual expansion of this idea so that, in association with recreational centers in a number of cities such as Philadelphia, Baltimore, Portland, and Cleveland, day camps are now available to elderly people during the summer months. These programs have been successful in offering vacation opportunities to many people who have never been able to get away from their homes before. In Baltimore, the campers were chosen from recipients of Old-Age Assistance, social security, and low incomes from other sources. Applicants were given a physical examination before acceptance and the average age of the group was 73 years. The program director, from the Department of Recreation, organized the campers into cabin units, with delegation of many of the administrative responsibilities to these unit leaders. Camp periods were scheduled so as to utilize the children's summer camp at the end of the season. Campers were enthusiastic in their reception of the program, and a further expansion is anticipated.

In Menlo Park, California, the Peninsula Volunteers, in 1949, established a recreational center called "Little House." The group, which began with 12 people, rapidly expanded so that it outgrew its quarters, and, in 1954, a special building was designed and constructed for the program. In Syracuse, New York, the "Wagon Wheel," a long-established community center for older people, has placed a great deal of emphasis on hobby craft. Currently, 1,800 persons are enrolled in its programs. Many older people have been led to develop skills which they never knew they possessed.

Although the desirability of providing recreational activities for older people cannot be denied, it would seem preferable to incorporate into these programs some activities that would offer benefit to the total community. One program that is outstanding in this respect is that of the Recreational Center for Older People in San Francisco, under the direction of Miss Florence Vickery. Although the social aspects are by no means neglected in this center, the older people have developed activities which are of benefit to other institutions. For example, in handicraft shops, they make useful items of apparel for patients in the city hospitals. They have also organized a service to visit shut-ins, sick, and elderly people in the city, as well as those confined in chronic disease hospitals. Special equipment and toys are made for the cerebral palsy school by older men who utilize the woodworking and shop facilities of the center, which is located in the Aquatic Park in San Francisco. The community services provided by the aged participants give vigor and purpose to the program. Communities anticipating the establishment of Golden Age Clubs and recreational centers for older people should give serious consideration to this aspect of the program.

In some cities, such as New York, Cleveland, and Syracuse, hobby shows have been organized, with special emphasis on the activities of older people. In New York, the Hobby Show has resulted in the establishment of an Elder Craftsmen Shop where the productions of older people are placed on sale on a commission basis. Competent people in merchandising aid in the selection of materials offered for sale in the shop. Members of the National Home Fashions League contribute their services in offering designs to gifted craftsmen to promote the quality of items made by the elderly.

In 1956, the New York State Legislature recognized recreation for older people as a proper municipal function by making state funds available, on a matching basis, to cities in the state that wished to initiate social programs. Responsibility for recommending approval of grants was placed in the hands of a State Council on Recreation for the Elderly, appointed by the Commissioner of Education.

Community services.—As indicated in previous chapters, the rising interest in the aging has led a large number of communities throughout the country to conduct surveys of the needs of the aged and of the resources available for meeting them.[13] One of the most extensive studies of this kind was carried out between 1947 and 1951 in Chicago.[14] Financed by the Wieboldt Foundation of Chicago, this study, published in 1952, not only summarizes the problems, but offers a plan of action for their solution. In common with many other subsequent studies, it was found that first in the consciousness of older people was the double problem of employment and retirement. Housing and health needs were not far behind, and finally the problems of activities and interpersonal relations were commonly mentioned by older people interviewed in the course of this study.

In New York, a study, financed by the Russell Sage Foundation, was conducted by Cornell University to answer the following questions: (1) What social and cultural factors facilitate adjustment to aging? (2) What kinds of people successfully adjust themselves to aging? (3) What forms should be taken by programs designed to serve the needs of the aged? The study, carried out in the Kips Bay–Yorkville Health District of New York, has been reported in detail.[15] This study has placed a primary emphasis on health needs and the utilization of counseling services for older people.

These surveys are representative of general findings and do not, by any means, exhaust the list. One observation that crops up repeatedly is that frequently there are available, within the framework of social agencies in a city, many services which could be utilized by older people. However, even among social workers there is often a lack of knowledge of the facilities available, and one of the major difficulties is that older people themselves are not aware of the existence of these services. Consequently, one important development has been the formation of central information services, frequently organized within the Council of Social Agencies in a city, which identify the types of services available.[16]

Communities are beginning to recognize that a wide variety of services is desirable for older people and that many of these services can be provided within the framework of current organization if effective methods of coordinating them are developed. Thus, family service agencies are prepared by function to meet specific problems of older people such as counseling and selection for placement in homes for the aged, or nursing homes, where such services are necessary. The Council of Jewish Social Agencies has shown leadership in integrated programs of counseling, medical care, home services, foster homes, and total aid to the elderly. The variety of problems encountered demands a high degree of flexibility. At the present time, it is doubtful whether any single community in the United States offers a complete program. On the premise that the elderly should remain in their own homes as long as possible, a number of communities now offer home care programs. These programs may range from periodic visits by a visiting nurse to simple aids in having someone help the older people do their marketing. For older people who are home-bound, programs of friendly visitors have been found effective. Although this service can be provided by volunteers, it has been found necessary to offer some training and supervision. The American Public Welfare Association and the Visiting Nurse Association of Peoria, Illinois, for example, have prepared effective material for use in this field.[17] A number of welfare agencies are able to provide home-maker services. For the most part, these services have been available for only temporary periods when there is acute illness. However, we know that many older people would remain in their own homes if a regular part-time home-maker service were available, in which a person would spend a few hours each week in performing household duties. The effectiveness of this service has been demonstrated by the New York City Department of Welfare.

In a few cities, such as Syracuse, New York, and Philadelphia, volunteer agencies have a service, used in Great Britain, which has been of great usefulness. This service, known as "Meals-on-Wheels," brings to the home of the aged individual, or couple, a completely prepared hot meal. One such service was started by the Lighthouse, a Red Feather Settlement House in a congested industrial section of Philadelphia, in January 1954. Volunteers at the Lighthouse package and personally deliver to selected clients, within a radius of about two miles, a thermos-insulated hot meal for noontime and a cold meal to be saved for supper. Potential clients are referred to the service from the Visiting Nurse Society, from local hospitals, by social workers at the Lighthouse, and from the Department of Public Assistance. After screening by social workers, acceptable clients are examined medically and psychologically. They are charged a weekly fee for the service, which varies from $2.00 to $5.00 according to their ability to pay. At intervals of about three months, clients are re-examined. Preliminary results indicate an improvement in physical and psychological well-being.

A "Sitter Service" for chronic invalids who are being cared for by their families is useful in relieving the strain on the persons providing care by giving them an opportunity to get away from home for business or recreation without constant worry about the invalid. One such service has been organized by two social workers in Hyde Park, Chicago, who take responsibility for recruiting and training responsible sitters. In planning for this kind of service, we must recognize that much more than "sitting" is involved. The duties require careful training and supervision.

The development and organization of these services require imagination. Many of them can be offered by the more able-bodied among the aging group. In this connection, the program initiated in Peoria, Illinois, whereby middle-aged and older women are given training by the existing social agencies for these services is of considerable significance.

In some communities, organizations of older people themselves are devoting their energies to community projects; one example is the Senior League of Hartford, Connecticut. This group meets first for discussion of community problems and selects activities for which their talents are appropriate. The membership is made up of citizens over the age of 50.

Summary.—The past five years have shown a remarkable growth in the recognition of community responsibility for integrated programs for the aged. Although the state and federal governments are playing an active role in stimulating community programs, a basic premise is that action programs should originate within the local community. It is also apparent that, although certain specialized services are desirable for older people, many of their needs can be met within the framework of present welfare activities if adequate coordination is effected. The trend in social work is to bring services to the older individual within his own home. Although no single community offers, as yet, a full and complete program, many are moving in this direction.

9

TRENDS IN | RESEARCH

As indicated in Chapter 1, solution of the complex problems in gerontology will require the application of research techniques of practically every scientific discipline. Previous chapters have raised many questions for which we have no final answers. In some instances, they are questions of fact, and in others, they involve projections and interpretations. Certainly, many of the questions of fact can be answered by research methods. It is beyond the scope of this volume to attempt to summarize, in detail, all of our knowledge about aging. However, a few bench marks in various aspects of aging will be described to give some point of reference for assessing research trends.

What is research?—Webster defines research as (1) careful search, a close searching; (2) studious inquiry; usually critical and exhaustive investigation or experimentation having for its aim the revision of accepted conclusions, in the light of newly discovered facts. The first definition is not very helpful, since it describes only a method of searching and offers no implication about finding anything. Some cynics are of the opinion that this definition characterizes research in aging. I disagree with both the implication and the definition. The key part of the definition of research is "having for its aim the revision of accepted conclusions." This means that to be effective research must be directed toward a specific question. Research is a technical operation and not all questions can be answered in the form asked. Many broad and general questions of great social importance must be broken down into simpler and more specific questions before they can be adequately attacked by research methods. This formulation of questions and the design of adequately controlled procedures and observations are the essence of research. It is unfortunately true that the greater the social significance of a question, the less apt it is to be answerable in terms of tightly designed experiments. However, many of these broad, important questions can be broken down into a series of more sharply focused questions which can be studied. In the physical sciences, the broad, general questions are formulated only after a great deal of specific experimental information is available. In gerontology, the reverse is true. We are being asked the broad, important questions before we have built up much of a backlog of answers to the small specific detailed questions.

The mere accumulation of information, valuable as it is, lacks one essential characteristic of research, namely, the determination of the interrelationships of two or more variables. The investigator wants to know not only what happens, but how it happens. Oftentimes, the first step in a research program is to find out what happens. At the present time, a large share of the research on aging is at this stage. Until we know what happens with aging, whether it be a social group, an individual, or even a cell, we are not in a position to answer the question of "how," since the design of experiments to answer this will depend upon making some preliminary guesses or hypotheses. In some research areas, as for example biology and physiology, we are beginning to see studies that attempt to find out how age changes occur.

Goals of research in aging.—One of the goals of gerontological research is to arrive at an understanding of the aging process. We want to find out why it is that the probability of death increases with age. We want to know the conditions which will influence this probability, whether they are genetic in character, or environmental in origin. We want to know the time sequences and the interrelationships of changes in different characteristics. We want to know what aging people are like, and why they behave the way they do. These are the broad questions which must be made more specific in order to be investigated. Thus, for example, we can find out how kidney function changes with age, and we can determine the factors that influence it. We cannot, however, infer that findings with respect to kidney function will be equally applicable to age changes in the performance of the heart, nervous system, or musculature. Each question must first be investigated separately in order to identify the factors that are common to a number of them.

Since aging is a process, it can be understood only by making observations over the entire life span. Although some questions can be answered by studying different individuals at each age level, many problems will require observations on the same individual at progressive intervals of the life span. Such longitudinal studies are expensive and difficult to carry out, particularly in the human. Aging cannot be studied where observations are made only on older animals or people. The essence of gerontological research is that comparisons must be made between organisms at least at two points in their life span, after the attainment of maturity.

Since the mortality curve is one index of aging, we must recognize the influence of disease in limiting life span. Although it is usually assumed that diseases which have a greater prevalence in later life are of primary importance, it is probable that nonfatal diseases experienced in early life also play a role in limiting the life span of the individual. Therefore, whatever information is gained with regard to the etiology and prevention of all diseases will have a direct and important bearing on mortality. Since effective research programs on specific diseases are already receiving attention and support, it is unnecessary to include them in the framework of gerontological research. In a pragmatic sense, separation of disease and aging is unnecessary, even if it were possible. Our best research approach would be simply to describe populations of aging people. If researchers had available random samples of the total population, this would be possible. However, most investigators can study only people who have already been selected, usually with a bias for the inclusion of disease states. Thus, it is often necessary to separate subjects into disease categories on the basis of our best methods for clinical evaluation. This, of course, does not guarantee the exclusion of subjects with early disease states, but it makes observations more comparable with the general population.

Over-all research progress.—The past five years have seen a marked impetus to research in gerontology. For example, the bibliography of published articles on gerontology identified some 15,000 references that had been published between about 1900 (some considerably earlier than this) and 1948.[1] Between 1949 and 1955, in a period of seven years, as many articles were published as had appeared in the previous 50-odd years.[2] Furthermore, the character of writing has changed significantly. The past seven years have shown a very marked increase in the number of experimental studies, in both the biological and the social sciences. Although a large proportion of the publications in gerontological research represents by-products from other investigations, more and more laboratories are developing systematic research programs on aging (see Chapter 10). These laboratories have greatly expanded our knowledge, particularly in the areas of physiology, biochemistry, and psychology. A part of the increase in publications can be ascribed to the more generous financial support for studies of cardiovascular diseases, cancer, and arthritis. Research in the social sciences has also been expanded. Many descriptive studies of community populations have appeared. In addition, a number of analytical studies have been initiated to identify the individual and community factors that contribute to the adjustment of the aging individual.

In 1940, Dr. E. J. Stieglitz[3] made a survey of research on aging that was being planned by investigators throughout the country. One hundred fourteen investigators, located in 70 laboratories, reported plans for specific research projects in the field of aging. In 1948, only 15 of the investigators who had responded to the previous questionnaire were actually working on problems relating to aging. Since 1948, there has been a notable increase in the number of laboratories in the United States that devote a major share of their research efforts to aging (see Chapter 10).

In 1948, Dr. A. I. Lansing[4] analyzed the 57 original papers published in the *Journal of Gerontology* in 1946 and 1947. Of the total 57 original papers, 27, or 47 percent, contained observational data in the biological and clinical sciences. Only one paper in experimental psychology was published during this time, and approximately 53 percent were concerned with general statements of aims, goals, and hopes for future research in gerontology. When the content of the

Journal of Gerontology between 1952 and 1956 was analyzed, an entirely different picture was obtained. The percentage of pages devoted to general discussions diminished from 22 percent in 1952 to around 4 percent in 1955 and 1956. This, of course, was partly a reflection of editorial policy to give preference to experimental studies within the limited space available in the journal, but it does mean that more experimental articles were submitted for publication. The space devoted to studies from the social sciences fluctuated between 6 and 20 percent over this five-year interval. Fifteen to 20 percent of the journal pages were devoted to articles in clinical medicine. This is not an indication of the level of research activity in the clinical sciences, since other journals were established which placed primary emphasis on geriatrics. Except for 1956, 30–40 percent of the space in the journal was used for publications in the field of physiology. Some of these articles, which have been classified under physiology, might also be regarded as clinical in nature, since a good share of them were concerned with studies on humans. Whenever selection of the subjects was primarily oriented toward normal individuals free from diagnosable disease, the articles were regarded as more physiological than clinical. Perhaps the most striking change in research publications in the journal, over these years, is the gradual increase in studies on basic biology, rising from a low of 9 percent in 1953 to a total of 26 percent in 1956. A somewhat similar increment in the field of psychology is also shown over this same period, so that, in 1956, some 20 percent of the journal pages were devoted to experimental studies in psychology.

New research workers.—According to Dr. A. I. Lansing's tabulation in 1948, there were only two investigators less than 50 years of age who were apparently committed to long-range studies of aging, as reflected in publications in the *Journal of Gerontology*. Although approximately 70 percent of the articles published in the *Journal of Gerontology* between 1952 and 1956 originated from investigators who had been concerned with research in aging prior to 1950, a substantial number of new investigators less than 50 years of age were included in the other 30 percent. Not counting individuals who appeared as collaborators and whose future research careers are uncertain, a rough estimate indicated 11 new workers in physiology, 7 in cellular biology,

10 in psychology, 10 in the social sciences, and 6 in clinical medicine; making a total of 44 new investigators in the field of aging. As indicated in Chapter 10, there are additional new investigators working on the problems of aging who have not yet brought their studies to publication. While this growth is far short of what we would like to envisage over the next five years, it indicates that research in aging is far from senescent.

Trends in research support.—As indicated in the first edition of *Trends in Gerontology*,[5] one of the primary needs for research in aging is stable, long-term financial support. The number of laboratories in the United States where young investigators may pursue research careers in gerontology has increased somewhat during the past five years. However, many projects are still supported by research grants which are made on an annual basis, although there is an increasing tendency to make longer commitments for gerontological studies, up to a maximum moral commitment of five years. Since investigations of aging may require long periods of incubation, the only solution to this problem is the organization of research institutes on gerontology with stable financial support, either within the framework of regular university or laboratory budgets, or as endowments for professorships of gerontology within existing university departments. Large funds for biological and medical research, particularly on specific diseases such as infantile paralysis, tuberculosis, heart disease, hypertension, and cancer, are now being raised by popular subscription. With increasing public realization of the problems of aging and the shift in the age of the population, there is almost certain to be an increasing public demand for support of research on the chronic and degenerative diseases. We should be looking forward and planning now for future expansion by training young investigators so that these problems can be studied on a fundamental level by competent researchers. It is important that research should not be stampeded into the search for a cure for some specific disease, as may readily happen if scientists are unprepared.

In 1954, the Bio-Sciences Information Exchange published an analysis of the support of research for the years 1952–53. The data for the report were taken from information on funds awarded for nonsecurity classified studies by seven government agencies (Atomic Energy Commission, Department of the Air Force, Department of the Army, Department of the Navy, National Science Foundation, Public Health Service, and the Veterans Administration), funds awarded by the national offices of major fund-raising organizations, and awards made by private foundations on a nation-wide scale.[6] In 1950, approximately $33,000,000 from government and nongovernment sources were distributed among 3,317 grantees. In 1950, there were approximately 76 projects supported to the extent of $982,000 that were classified as pertinent to aging. By 1953, the total number of grants had increased to almost 5,000, amounting to 56 million dollars. Of this total, 127, with financial support of 1.4 million dollars, represented research in aging. It should be pointed out that the classification used by the Bio-Sciences Information Exchange includes, under age studies, investigations dealing with growth and development, studies of disease processes in older people, as well as projects concerned with the aging process. Of the 127 projects identified in 1953 as concerned with aging, only about one-third dealt specifically with gerontology as defined in Chapter 1. Thus, it is obvious that, although there has been an increase in the support of gerontological research, the increment since 1950 has not been proportional to the total increase in research funds for the biosciences as a whole. The tabulation of projects on aging, prepared by Dr. J. E. Birren,[7] shows that research in gerontology was concentrated primarily in departments of physiology, pathology, and biochemistry of medical schools, and that almost half of the studies utilized humans as experimental material; rats and mice accounted for about one-fourth of the studies.

Another index of trends in research support is afforded by analysis of grants made through the Division of Research Grants and Fellowships of the National Institutes of Health. In this analysis, studies of disease processes have been excluded even though their importance in limiting life span is recognized. Only those studies in which age is considered by the investigator as one variable have been included. Any study meeting this criterion was tabulated even though only part of the total project was concerned with aging. In the fiscal year 1951–52, there was a total of 17 projects, with support of approximately

$250,000.[8] This represented approximately 1 percent of the total number of grants and 1.3 percent of the total funds allocated by the Division of Research Grants in 1951–52. A similar analysis, conducted on grants made between July 1, 1955 and July 1, 1956, identified 65 projects, with a total support of almost $600,000.[9] Fifteen of these projects were concerned with problems of cellular biology, physiology, and genetics. Six additional projects dealt with anatomical changes in aging animals or people. The general area of human physiology received primary support, with 22 projects. Clinical disease and aging in individuals accounted for 12 projects. Experimental psychology and problems of social adjustment were represented by 6 projects, and the general area of sociology by 4. Although a large proportion of the grants went to laboratories that had been interested over a long period of years in aging, about 20 percent of the projects, and some 35 percent of the total funds, went to investigators who were new to the field since 1951. From this analysis, we see that there has been an increment in interest and support of research projects in basic biology and physiology, as well as in experimental psychology and sociology. However, we must admit that although there has been an increment in research in aging, its magnitude is not commensurate with the increase in research interest in more clinical or disease-oriented studies. However, it should be pointed out that there is a source of support for research in the basic sciences, and its exploitation is dependent primarily upon the interest of investigators throughout the country.

In order to stimulate research on aging, the Ciba Foundation established, in 1954, an annual award for significant research contributions to aging. The award is made by a committee of distinguished scientists on the basis of unpublished manuscripts submitted by investigators from all parts of the world. From some 75 submitted manuscripts, the top award was made to Dr. S. M. Friedman of the University of British Columbia in 1955 and to Drs. M. Keech and R. Reid jointly, of the University of Leeds, England, in 1956.

Recognizing the importance of basic research on aging, the National Institutes of Health established, in July 1956, a Center for Research on Aging. This center, under the direction of Dr. G. Halsey

Hunt, has as one of its assignments the encouragement of research programs in gerontology. Although the center has no special funds to allocate, Dr. Hunt and his professional staff are prepared to work with universities and investigators interested in studies on aging, to aid them in the details of preparing research proposals for submission to the Division of Research Grants and Fellowships.

Although there are relatively few fellowships in gerontology, the National Institute of Mental Health has, over the past five years, supported six fellows. In addition, a number of pharmaceutical manufacturers have established fellowships in gerontology and geriatrics. There is still a great need for support in this area, particularly for predoctoral fellows to aid in the training of future research workers in gerontology.

Gerontology owes a great debt to the Josiah Macy, Jr. Foundation, since it was through the vision of this Foundation that a subsidy was provided which made possible the publication of the volume *Problems of Ageing*, edited by Dr. E. V. Cowdry.[10] It was also the Josiah Macy, Jr. Foundation which, in 1940, provided an initial grant to the United States Public Health Service for the establishment of what is now the Gerontology Branch of the National Heart Institute. Its sponsorship of the Conferences on Aging (1938–53) and the publication of the proceedings did much to further research in gerontology at a time when few people were interested. The Foundation, through a grant-in-aid, supported Dr. Lansing's early studies on aging in the rotifer; it aided Dr. Clive McCay in pursuing his studies on aging and nutrition and aided Dr. H. S. Simms in his studies of mortality in rats and mice. With the rise in governmental support of research following World War II, private foundations were not inclined to support laboratory studies. However, the situation has been changing, and during the past five years a number of private foundations such as the W. K. Kellogg Foundation, the McGregor Fund of Detroit, the Frederick and Amelia Schimper Foundation, the Rockefeller Foundation, the Ford Foundation, the E. D. Farmer Foundation, the Dors Foundation, the Russell Sage Foundation, the Twentieth Century Fund, the Lilly Endowment, and the Forest Park Foundation have made grants for research on aging.

Availability of experimental material.—In 1950, there were very few laboratories which maintained animals throughout their life span. Dr. H. S. Simms had a large colony of rats and mice, Dr. Clive McCay maintained rats and was beginning his dog colony; Dr. L. C. Strong, then at Yale, and the group at Bar Harbor maintained mice, and Dr. James B. Rogers, at the University of Louisville, had an extensive colony of guinea pigs. Other investigators were dependent upon securing aged animals from retired breeding stocks and from other sources on a sporadic basis. It is now recognized that the maintenance of animal colonies over long periods of time is essential for gerontological research. Consequently, many research grants now contain funds for such purposes. As a result, there has been a very marked expansion in the maintenance of aged animals.

Although there is still a serious limitation in the availability of old animals, the situation is definitely improving. Older animals can be purchased from commercial farms. However, because of the great influence of diet, temperature, infection, etc., over the life span of an animal, most investigators prefer to rear and maintain their own animals. The University of Wisconsin has recently established a research project which plans to make longitudinal studies on monkeys whose life span is estimated as something between 15 and 20 years. Although major emphasis in this program will be placed on the long-term effects of radiation, the study will offer important gerontological information, since control groups, free of radiation, must also be followed.

Most old-age studies on humans have been limited to institutional populations of one kind or another, and there are, no doubt, grave sampling errors present in much of our so-called knowledge of aging. Although institutional groups may be of great value in the development of techniques and procedures, it is obvious that until we are able to test a wide variety of individuals, living within the community, our knowledge of aging in human beings remains biased and unsatisfactory. During the past five years, there has been a marked expansion in the utilization for research of patients in chronic disease hospitals and in old people's homes. More important, significant progress in studies of the aging has been made in recruiting individuals from communities. At present, most of these studies are concerned with psychological and sociological problems. With the development of Golden Age Clubs, there is a great opportunity to extend our research contacts with people living in the community. We must place major emphasis on educational programs to acquaint middle-aged and older adults with the importance of their assistance in serving as subjects for research. It has been estimated that 30 percent of the population now above the age of 65 years owe their lives to the advances in medicine in public health, as well as in general public welfare, which have been made since they were born. For many of the advances in medicine, we are indebted to medical students who gave of their time and blood for these investigations. Similarly, if we are to solve the problem of diseases of later life, many middle-aged and elderly people must be willing to make contributions of their time, money, and even of their own blood so that science may progress. The success of Dr. Ancel Keys and his associates in recruiting volunteers from Minneapolis and St. Paul for his laboratory studies on aging and the etiology of cardiovascular diseases is a welcome sign that the public, when adequately informed of the needs, will respond to the call.

In many research studies, large groups of subjects are necessary. Consequently, for efficiency, this means that the testing procedures must be set up in environments where large groups of individuals are available. Studies on growth and development of the child flourished only when investigators and research institutes developed appropriate contacts with school authorities which permitted access to school children. In the case of adults, the comparable situation is in the factory or office. Consequently, research in aging could be given a major impetus if collaboration were arranged with departments of industrial relations. Such departments have developed contacts with both management and labor which would be invaluable in securing access to large groups of individuals in factories and offices. The effective organization of any such programs will, of course, depend upon securing the confidence and cooperation of labor leaders as well as representatives of management. Such collaborative arrangements have already been established in a number of universities such as the University of California, the University of Chicago, and the University of Wisconsin.

Research on the biology of aging.—In 1953, Dr. T. S. Gardner made a comparison of chapters from the three editions of *Cowdry's Problems of Ageing*[12] and concluded that research on the basic biology of aging was practically at a standstill.[13] This analysis was based upon the new references added to each chapter in the third edition, i.e., references dated 1942 and after. This criterion is inadequate, since authors of chapters in the third edition varied considerably with respect to the amount of rewriting and re-evaluation that was done. For example, chapters prepared by new authors for the third edition showed a much higher percentage of references dated after 1942 than did the chapters prepared by the original authors of the first and second editions.

Although research in basic biology still needs support and expansion, it cannot be said that no progress is being made.

For example, Dr. Alex Comfort[14] has published an excellent summary of research on the biological aspects of senescence. On the basis of his summary of the literature, Dr. Comfort concludes that various factors, in varying proportions, contribute to the senile changes in different species. Among the factors that contribute to senescence are the deterioration of irreplaceable structures, the sum of previous injuries which are imperfectly repaired, and progressive morphogenic changes in the nature and specificity of cellular responses and organ functions. To Dr. Comfort, senescence is not an "inherent" property of animals (other than unicellular organisms like bacteria, yeasts, etc.), but one which they have acquired as a potentiality probably through the operation of evolutionary forces directed toward other biological goals.

We know that the longevity of the animal is determined, in part, by genetic factors. A number of experiments have shown clearly that strains of fruit flies with widely different life spans could be isolated by selective breeding. Similarly, Dr. A. I. Lansing was able to show that some cytoplasmic factor was involved in his experiments on longevity of the rotifer. In these experiments, the offspring from young mothers lived longer than those from old. Furthermore, this increase in longevity was cumulative over successive generations. More recently, Dr. Morris Rockstein has shown a similar effect in flies. Matings between long-lived mice have shown that longevity is a characteristic that is determined, at least in part, by parental influences. Dr. F. Kallmann's studies[15] on old twins, as well as Dr. Raymond Pearl's earlier studies on humans, indicate that similar factors operate in the human.

Although aging and death of the individual occur in all animal species, the pattern of aging depends on the species. In lower animal forms such as reptiles and fish, individuals continue to increase in size throughout their life. In contrast, warm-blooded mammals grow rapidly during early life, show a period of fairly uniform size after attaining sexual maturity, and finally go through a decline that ends with death. Warm-blooded animals show evidences of declining physiological functions as maturity progresses. For example, the number of eggs laid by birds and the number of young born in each litter gradually diminish with age. In contrast, the cold-blooded animals, which continue to grow throughout their life and often live to advanced ages, do not show reductions in physiological function. The number of eggs laid by snakes rises progressively with age. Since the metabolism of cold-blooded animals drops to low levels during cold weather, the differences in longevity between cold- and warm-blooded animals, which maintain a uniform temperature and higher metabolic rates, have been ascribed to differences in the "rate of living." The fact that the life span of many small aquatic animals, as well as insects, can be shortened by keeping their body temperature slightly elevated is also cited as evidence for the "rate of living" theory of aging.

Shortening of the life span by overfeeding has been demonstrated in silkworms and in a number of small aquatic animals. In rats and mice, restriction of caloric intake, beginning early in life, retards the growth rate, but extends the life span significantly. In the classic experiments carried out by Dr. Clive McCay, groups of rats were restricted to about half the caloric intake that they would normally consume. These rats, although stunted in growth, lived much longer than their well-fed brothers and sisters. Although we know, from insurance statistics, that overweight in the human shortens life expectancy, we can scarcely apply the results of Dr. McCay's studies to human populations. Nevertheless, these experiments indicate the importance of nutrition to longevity.

In the past few years, there has been a rising interest in the effects of radiation on life span. It has been claimed that sublethal doses of radiation have resulted in premature aging in rats. If premature aging is defined as a reduction in average length of life, this statement cannot be denied. However, it has not yet been determined whether radiation, either in single doses or in small doses distributed over the life span of the animal, induces the same kind of changes as those which occur spontaneously with age. Nevertheless, the interest of radiobiologists has given considerable impetus to studies of aging. This is partly because good life tables on substantial numbers of animals are available in only a few species such as the mouse, the rat, the fish, and the human. Although the literature abounds with reports of single animals of various species that have lived a specified number of years,[16] this information is subject to large errors and is of little value in assessing the effects of experimental conditions on life span. For this, a detailed life table on a substantial number of animals is essential.

Age changes in structural tissues and cells.—Conventional microscopic methods have shown only minor changes in cellular structure with age.[17] Thus, for example, cells of the nervous system are often found with an accumulation of pigments, which apparently increase with age. These pigments have not been identified with regard to chemical structure, and are simply known as "age pigments" on the assumption that they represent an accumulation of waste products. In certain specific tissues, such as the pituitary gland, there are age differences in the staining characteristics of cellular components. Age pigments are also reported in cardiac and skeletal muscle.

When more detailed examinations were made with the use of the electron microscope, alterations in structure of certain cellular components such as the mitrochondria were found. However, other factors, such as diet and infections, will apparently produce similar changes even in the cells of young animals, so that we cannot ascribe these reported changes to age alone. No doubt with the development of new techniques and the use of immunological methods, whereby specific compounds can be identified within cells, we are on the threshold of important new discoveries.

Microscopic examination of tissue slices of many organs of the body show age changes. The characteristic change is an increase in the connective tissue and other substances that surround individual cells, and in some tissues, such as the nervous system, there is an actual disappearance of cellular elements. Thus, aged tissues tend to show increased amounts of connective tissue, fat, and other extracellular substances, and, in some tissues, a reduction in the number of normally functioning cells. In muscle tissue, for example, a gradual reduction in the diameter of the muscle fibers has been reported. In peripheral nerves, the number of fibers diminishes in the old animal. Although we have the picture of cellular loss and the accumulation of connective tissue in older animals, we are limited, for the most part, to descriptive statements. We need to apply improved techniques that will give us more quantitative data to specify the degree of these changes with age.

Another characteristic of aging is the gradual loss of elastic properties of connective tissue. Since connective tissue is present in all organs, an understanding of these changes has general significance. Studies have shown that, with increasing age, there is an increase in the fiber content of connective tissue with a reduction in the gel phase. Recently, attention has also been focused on the importance of materials surrounding cells in tissues, the so-called ground substance. Investigations of these extracellular components are important, since all substances which enter or leave each cell must pass through them.

Age changes in cellular metabolism.—As our knowledge of biochemistry has expanded, methods for the assay of specific enzyme systems have become more precise. As a result, a number of investigators have been studying the activity of specific enzymes in tissues from animals of various ages. Most of this work has been done on the rat and the guinea pig, but a few studies have been possible on blood vessels removed from humans at autopsy. The over-all rate of metabolism of a tissue is reflected in its rate of utilizing oxygen. A number of studies have shown that the rate of oxygen utilization is lower in old tissues (kidney, muscle) than in young. These studies have, however, failed to determine the actual number of living cells that were present in the tissue slice on which the determination was made. Since there is often a loss of cells in tissues of old animals, we cannot conclude that the metabolic activity of each cell in the tissue or organ of the old animal has necessarily diminished. A number of investigators are attempting to devise methods for determining the number of cells present in a tissue preparation. Preliminary results indicate that the activity of certain specific enzymes may diminish at a more rapid rate than cells that are lost in some tissues which are no longer capable of forming new cells. There are, however, literally hundreds of enzymes in each cell which contribute to the life process. Some of them are concerned with the production of energy, whereas others are concerned with the synthesis of complex protein molecules which are necessary to the existence of each cell. All of these systems are interrelated, so that it is not possible to assign primary importance to any one of them for the maintenance of life. Our problem can be answered only by detailed systematic studies, many of which will, no doubt, yield negative results. This information, in itself, is important, as we can thereby exclude certain systems from further consideration. At present, the biochemical studies are limited to a relatively few laboratories, but there are signs of a rising recognition among biochemists in general of aging as an important biological problem.

Age changes in the physiological performance of various organ systems.—We have learned a great deal in the past five years about the age changes in the performance of a number of specific organ systems.[18] Results obtained in the study of kidney function illustrate a number of points that are common to other organ systems as well. Figure 9 illustrates the age changes in the amount of blood perfusing the kidney per minute. The blood flow through the kidney, as measured by diodrast or PAH clearance, shows an average decrease from age 30 onward. The subjects tested were carefully selected by medical examination to exclude any individuals with identifiable kidney

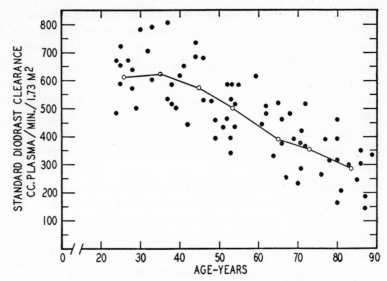

Fɪɢ. 9—Change in standard diodrast clearance or effective renal plasma flow with age. Data from N. W. Shock, Chap. 23 in A. I. Lansing (ed.), *Cowdry's Problems of Ageing*, 3d ed. (Baltimore, Williams & Wilkins Co., 1952), p. 621.

disease. The average decline, of approximately 6 percent per decade, proceeds at a linear rate. There is no evidence of a sudden drop in kidney function at any specific chronological age. Furthermore, the data illustrate the wide individual differences in the effects of age on a physiological function. Thus, some people in their eighties still have kidney function as good as the average 40-year-old. Aging, therefore, is a highly individual matter, and chronological age is a poor predictor of what physiological performance may be expected. A similar decrement was also observed in the maximum amount of diodrast, or PAH, that can be excreted by the kidney per unit of time.

Similar linear decrements in performance with age have been observed in other organ systems. For example, the amount of blood pumped by the heart under resting conditions, the average speed of conduction of a nerve impulse in a peripheral nerve, the maximum amount of air that can be expired from the lungs, the maximum amount of air that can be moved through the lungs in a specified interval of time, muscular strength, and excretion of certain hormones produced by sex glands and the adrenal glands all show gradual decrements with increasing age.

On the other hand, certain physiological characteristics are closely regulated under resting conditions, even at advanced ages. Thus there is no evidence for systematic changes in the acidity of the blood, the sugar content of the blood, and the total volume of blood present in the body, or the capacity to absorb orally administered vitamin A.

Although these characteristics are well maintained under resting conditions, it has been shown that, when physiological stress is applied which displaces any of these characteristics from normal values, the rate of recovery is slower in the older individual than in the young. For example, the fasting blood sugar level remains quite constant even in old people, but when the level is increased by the intravenous administration of sugar, the older individual requires more time for readjustment. Similar observations have been made following the administration of acids or alkaline compounds in old and young subjects. We, therefore, have direct laboratory evidence that reserve capacities are significantly reduced in the older person.

Increasing age is accompanied by alterations in some, but not all, of the endocrine glands.[19] Thus, numerous studies have shown the gradual reduction in function of the sex glands. Since basal metabolism diminishes with increasing age, it has been assumed that the function of the thyroid gland, which plays a major role in regulating basal metabolism, also diminishes with age. However, careful examination of a number of indices of thyroid function, such as the amount of protein-bound iodine present in the plasma and the ability of the thyroid gland to remove iodine from the blood, fail to substantiate this assumption. Furthermore, experiments have shown that the thyroid gland in old people is still capable of responding to the physiological stimulus of the thyroid-stimulating hormone of the pituitary gland.

Laboratory studies of the adrenal gland have failed to demonstrate any marked changes in its functional capacity. When the adrenal cortical stimulating hormone of the pituitary was administered experimentally to old subjects, the responses with respect to metabolic changes were no different from those observed in young subjects. In the light of our present knowledge, it seems that some, but not necessarily all, of the endocrine glands are involved in age changes in the human. The physiological impairments that do occur with increasing age and, particularly, the reduction in reserve capacities which has been observed may be related, in part, to the gradual loss of functioning tissue. Consequently, problems of nutrition assume an important role in aging.

Metabolism and nutrition.—Studies on nutrition and metabolism follow two general lines of approach: one is the careful study of the ability of individuals to absorb and utilize various foodstuffs. These studies require elaborate laboratory techniques, and relatively few subjects can be observed. The second approach depends upon the survey of food habits, food intakes, and physiological status of large groups of subjects. Laboratory studies, using the metabolic balance technique, in which a detailed chemical analysis is made of everything entering the body and everything leaving, have indicated that normal older people, when given adequate intakes of specific food constituents, are able to absorb them and to build them into the tissues of their bodies. The important findings from these laboratory studies are that, although the nutritional requirements for older people may be slightly different than for middle-aged adults, the intake of proteins, minerals, and vitamins must be maintained in later life for healthy existence. Some investigators are of the opinion that the older individual must increase his intake of certain food materials, principally proteins, minerals, and vitamins, in order to ensure an adequate retention of these substances. The data are scanty and incomplete, and additional studies are required before we can give a final answer to this question.[20]

Although the total metabolism of the individual gradually diminishes with age, we cannot assume that the rate of metabolism of individual cells in the body of the old person is necessarily diminished. This is because, with age, there is an indeterminant diminution in the amount of functioning tissue. In order to answer the question of how much, we must have a great deal of additional research on the metabolism of individual cells.

Recent studies have shown clearly that there is a higher incidence of arteriosclerosis in populations where the fat content of the diet is high. This finding has led to the conclusion that a reduction in the fat intake will offer protection to the individual against the development of arteriosclerosis and therefore that the diet of older people ought to restrict the intake of fats. This presumption may or may not be true. At the present time, we do not have sufficient evidence to give a clear-cut answer to this question. Studies now in progress indicate further that saturated fats (largely from animal sources) probably play a greater role than unsaturated fats (largely from vegetable sources) in the development of arteriosclerosis.

As indicated previously, studies on a number of lower forms of animals have indicated that overnutrition tends to reduce life span. In the human, mortality statistics collected by life insurance companies show first of all that overweight in the adult reduces life expectancy, and second, that when body weight is reduced in an overweight population, the life expectancy improves. Overweight is primarily a problem of middle-age which is amenable to control. Statistics on the average weight of the population over age 60 are very scanty. Calculations have shown that in certain small samples of adult males, the lean body mass diminishes with age. The increments in total body weight represent primarily the gradual accumulation of fat and water.

Nutritional surveys of older people living in their own homes have been made in a number of communities. In some studies, as for example the San Mateo, California, study, correlations between indices of nutritional status and the diet have been attempted. In the California study, conducted on volunteers, some nutritional indices such as hemoglobin values, plasma protein, vitamin A, and carotene content of the plasma showed gradual declines with age. However, the correlation between the amount of decline and the dietary intake of an individual was very low. Dietary surveys, conducted in rural communities, fail to demonstrate any major inadequacies in the diet of older people. However, among low-income groups, particularly in cities, inadequate intakes of proteins, minerals, and vitamins have been reported among older people. They are prone to consume a higher proportion of their food in the form of carbohydrates, with a reduction in protein intake. Part of this is obviously related to income level, since protein foods are more expensive than carbohydrates. Other studies have indicated that poor dentition also contributes to the increased consumption of soft carbohydrate foods among the elderly. Older people are apt to have strong prejudices about their ability to digest and assimilate particular foods. When this happens, major imbalances in diets may easily occur. Thus, the problems of nutrition in the older person are not entirely physiological; they include elements of psychology, personality, and economics as well.

Medical research.—A number of excellent summaries and handbooks on the diseases of old age are available.[21] Dr. Robert T. Monroe has documented, in detail, the disease states observed in patients seen in his Geriatric Clinic in Boston.[22] A large proportion of the research funds available through private foundations and federal agencies is being devoted to studies of disease processes which are prevalent among older people. Thus, practically every medical school and teaching hospital in the United States is engaged in some research associated with diseases of the heart, blood vessels, or joints, with cancer or mental disease. Although many studies are concerned with the treatment of these diseases in older people, there has been a much greater emphasis on etiology and prevention. There is a rising belief that the prevention of the diseases of old age has important implications for public health. Although we do not have the final answers about methods for preventing arteriosclerosis, cancer, arthritis, or mental disease, a number of state health departments, as well as the Public Health Service, recognize that not all of our information is applied in an adequate fashion. Plans are being formulated for demonstration projects to develop health maintenance clinics for adults.

Many new developments in medicine are of direct benefit to aging people. Thus, for example, many older patients can now receive the benefits of surgery, if adequate precautions for anesthesia and post-surgical care are met. New developments in surgery permit the grafting of new blood vessels to preserve vitality in a limb which otherwise might be lost. Advances in endocrinology have shown that some older people may benefit both physically and mentally from male and female sex hormones when administered under the careful supervision of a physician. The introduction of cortisone and ACTH has contributed greatly to reducing the suffering among arthritic patients. The administration of steroid hormones can effectively reduce the rate of progression of osteoporosis. New antibiotics have greatly reduced the mortality from pneumonia, which was previously an important cause of death among elderly people. New drugs have been developed which make it possible to care for older patients with mild mental disturbances in their own homes—patients who previously would have needed commitment to a mental hospital. Of even greater importance is the recognition by physicians that a great deal can be done for older patients through application of medical knowledge and skills.

Psychological aspects of aging.—A number of reviews summarize the present state of our knowledge about the psychological aspects of aging.[23] One generalization common to many individual studies is that the speed of performance diminishes progressively with age. The decrement in speed of performance with age increases with the complexity of the task.[24] Older people have slower reaction times and even show a slight reduction in the speed of conduction of nerve impulses. It is also evident, from a number of studies, that the age decrement in performance is much less in tasks that are well practiced than in newly learned performances. Although many studies have shown age decrements in perception (visual, auditory), these impairments need not limit the performance of the older person, since adequate corrections in the form of glasses and hearing aids are possible.

Recent studies have shown that the previously reported decrements in intelligence, with age, are probably not as great as was originally indicated. Part of this decrement in older people can be ascribed to limitations in their educational background. Where the same individuals have been tested at increasing ages, the evidence now indicates that, at least up to the age of 35 or 40, intellectual capacity also expands rather than diminishes. Other studies have shown that the degree of impairment in intellectual capacity with age is greater among the less intelligent than among the more intelligent people. Thus, only a slight impairment in performance, when speed is not made a condition of the test, was found in professional groups such as engineers and college professors. As indicated in a previous chapter, there is no evidence that older people cannot learn. However, their rate of acquisition of a new skill is somewhat slower and is influenced by the degree of motivation. In older people, learning is apt to be slower because of interference from previously learned material. The degree and extent of this interference are still problems for future research. One serious limitation to evaluation of age changes in intelligence is that most of the tests now available depend, in large measure, on school skills. In adults, some of these skills are used only infrequently, and consequently limit performance. Psychologists are attempting to devise new tests which will minimize or eliminate this difficulty.

Although many specific examples of high achievements in the arts and sciences have been reported for people in advanced years, systematic surveys indicate that, particularly in the physical and biological sciences, outstanding achievements are more apt to occur at an early age than later.[25] In other areas of activity, however, for example politics and administration, the maturity and experience of a lifetime are important factors in determining achievement.

With the development of a questionnaire by Dr. E. W. Burgess and Dr. R. J. Havighurst[26] to assess social and personal adjustment, there have been a large number of studies utilizing this device. Although many factors have been shown to influence adjustment in old age, it seems apparent that the maintenance of interests and a broad spectrum of activities are the best insurance against maladjustment. Older people living in the community are more apt to be well adjusted than are those living in institutions. An adequate income is also a powerful factor in producing good adjustment. Although health status is a source of concern to all elderly people, the social and economic results of ill-health are of perhaps more importance than physical status itself.[27] Other studies have shown that the conception of increased rigidity and conservatism among older people has little basis in fact.

As indicated in a previous chapter, research has shown that work and retirement have a variety of meanings to adults.[28] The willingness to accept retirement is much more prevalent among industrial workers than among professional people. All of these findings have important implications for the organization of action programs in the field of aging.

Sociological research.—The past five years have seen a marked expansion in sociological research. Detailed surveys, based on both interviews and questionnaires, have been conducted in small cities and in rural areas.[28,29] These studies, coupled with those made in large city areas, highlight the effects of urbanization on the problems of the elderly. The acceptance of older people and their role in the community is markedly influenced by social status. These studies have found that older people wish to participate in community life.

The distribution of older people in the population, their places of residence, and projections of future numbers have been of increasing interest. A few studies of migration of the elderly have indicated a rising mobility of older people, with a tendency to gravitate to areas in the south and southwest parts of the United States. However, not all retired people have expressed a desire to move into areas of milder climate. Many prefer to remain within their own communities, so that, at present, the future trends in migration are confused.

Social work and counseling of older people have received considerable impetus. Demonstration projects have shown that employment counseling is effective with older people.

Studies on retirement indicate that, with adequate preparation, retirement can be attractive to a good number of older people. Although the mortality rate among retirees during the first two or three years after retirement is higher than would have been predicted from the age curve itself, it has not been proved that retirement itself leads to premature death. The high rates may simply be a reflection of the fact that a large share of 65-year-olds who retire voluntarily do so for reasons of ill-health. After the first two or three years, these people have dropped out of the population, so that in subsequent years the mortality rate among retirees is the same as that expected from the total population.

Summary.—From this brief résumé of the current status of research, it is apparent that significant advances have been made during the past few years. In terms of funds and workers available, the greatest research effort is directed toward the study of disease states. However, it is encouraging to note the increasing interest among biologists, physiologists, biochemists, and psychologists in some of the basic problems of aging. There has also been a notable increase in research on the sociological aspects of aging. We are still confronted with a good many unanswered questions such as "What is aging?" "What factors influence the rate of aging?" "How can disease incidence, mortality, and morbidity be reduced?" "What are the potential capacities of older people and how may they best be utilized to the good of society?" "What techniques will prove most effective in stimulating aging people to exercise their potential capacities?" "What are the factors that influence personal adjustment in older people?" "How do the personality and emotional characteristics of people change with age?" "What are the most appropriate methods of care for aged people when senility occurs?"

We still need a great deal of fundamental research in order to answer these questions. Public pressure for action programs is rising at a greater rate than is support of research. Consequently, we are already faced with the necessity for designing action programs without adequate information. We already see the effects of public pressure on the increased support for research on the diseases prevalent among the elderly. Disease-oriented studies are readily justified in contributing to public demand. There is, however, no guarantee that basic fundamental research on problems of aging will be agressively pursued unless laboratories are established for this express purpose. The pursuit of knowledge about the basic processes has been, and will undoubtedly continue to be, an activity of the universities. It is to scientists, who can pursue investigations without regard to the practical implications of applicability and the treatment of patients, that we must look for advances in our knowledge.

RESEARCH POTENTIALS

One index of research progress that can be anticipated is the number of laboratories and workers occupied with the study of aging. In the survey conducted in 1949, and reported in the first edition of *Trends in Gerontology*, only 17 laboratories were identified where aging represented a primary research interest. In addition, nine universities were at that time contemplating the organization of research programs in gerontology. During the past seven or eight years, there has been a marked change in the situation. Although a few of the laboratories investigating aging in 1949–50 have turned to other programs and some of the universities which were contemplating programs at that time have not made much progress, there has been a marked upturn in both the number of coordinated research programs on aging and in the number of individual investigators who have taken up the problem. A large share of the increased research activity can be attributed to the greater availability of financial support for research on aging through grants-in-aid from the federal government. In addition, the increased number of scientific conferences has brought to the attention of investigators the potentialities of research in aging. Interest is expanding at such a rapid rate that it is no longer possible to assure completeness in any listing of laboratories or investigators. However, the present chapter offers a brief description of laboratories with organized programs in aging, and investigators with continuing interest in gerontology.

RESEARCH CENTERS OR INSTITUTES NOW IN OPERATION

Washington University, St. Louis, Missouri.—St. Louis has long been a center of activity in various aspects of gerontology. Between 1939 and 1955, members of the staff of Washington University contributed 346 publications to the field of gerontology. Stemming from Dr. E. V. Cowdry's editorship of *Problems of Ageing* in 1939, activities in gerontology have spread throughout the Medical School and the university and within the community itself. Although a central coordinating committee has been formed in St. Louis,[1] there is no formal structure with respect to the various activities in gerontology. Educational programs for the aging are under the leadership of Dr. W. H. Reals. Research on the psychological aspects of aging is directed by Dr. Marion E. Bunch of the university and Dr. I. N. Mensh of the Psychology Department of the Medical School. In addition to his general interest in gerontology, Dr. Cowdry directs an operating research program at the Wernse Cancer Research Laboratory. In the Department of Anatomy, Dr. W. S. Hartroft is studying the influence of diet on age changes in the vascular system, and Dr. M. Trotter is interested in age changes in hair and anthropometric measurements. In the Department of Psychiatry, Dr. E. F. Gildea and his associates are investigating problems of adjustment of older people. The Division of Gerontology of the Medical School is under the leadership of Dr. J. E. Kirk and Dr. W. B. Kountz. In addition, investigations on some of the anatomical consequences of aging in rats are being made by Dr. and Mrs. M. Silberberg in the St. Louis City Hospitals, and on age changes in blood vessels by Dr. H. T. Blumenthal at the Jewish Hospital in St. Louis. Much of the basic biological research on aging was carried out by Dr. A. I. Lansing while a member of the staff of the Department of Anatomy. Dr. R. A. Moore, who is currently vice-chancellor of the University of Pittsburgh, was also influential in developing programs in gerontology at Washington University.

The Division of Gerontology of Washington University Medical School is supported, in part, by the income from a fund of $1,400,000 left to the university in 1948 by Mrs. Erbauer at the suggestion of Dr. W. B. Kountz. Income from this fund is used to pay part of the salaries of younger staff members in various departments of the Medical School, as for example Physiology, Anatomy, and Psychology. Members appointed to these positions carry out research programs on aging within the framework of the particular department. In addition, the fund supports basic research under the direction of Dr. J. E. Kirk, which is carried on in laboratories located in the Chronic Hospital and Old People's Home of St. Louis. Dr. Kirk and his colleagues have a primary interest in enzyme chemistry, and have made significant contributions to our knowledge about age changes in cellular metabolism. Age changes in basal metabolism, the infusion of lipids through the skin, and blood levels of various vitamins have also been reported by Dr. Kirk and his colleagues.

Dr. W. B. Kountz and Dr. Kirk have also developed a research program using the clinical material in the Chronic Hospital and Old People's Home. The City of St. Louis provides the necessary space and access to clinical material, but the direct costs of the research are met by the Division of Gerontology and by funds donated by grateful patients of Dr. Kountz. Through the efforts of Dr. Kountz, the Gerontological Research Foundation now receives gifts and donations which are used to support gerontological research in St. Louis and elsewhere. Dr. Kountz and his collaborators have been interested in metabolism and the nutritional aspects of aging. In collaboration with Dr. W. M. Allen and Dr. W. H. Masters of the Department of Obstetrics and Gynecology, important clinical studies on the effects of administering sex hormones to older people have been carried out. The Department of Psychology of the Medical School has collaborated in these studies by assessing the personality and intellectual changes subsequent to the administration of sex hormones.

In addition to research activities, Dr. Kountz supervises the medical care of patients in the Chronic Hospital. The resident staff is supported by the City of St. Louis. This is one of the few places in the United States where training and experience in geriatrics can be obtained by young physicians.

The Division of Gerontology of Washington University is one of the few institutes which have been established through endowment funds. This assures financial stability and continuity of support, which are so essential for effective research in gerontology. Because of the fluidity of funds, it has been possible to accept young investigators from outside the United States for periods of one or two years. This exchange of investigators has added to the effectiveness of the research and has offered valuable training experience. With its broad program, ranging from basic biochemistry to clinical investigations, this institute will undoubtedly continue to be a primary source of our expanding knowledge about aging.

The Department of Psychiatry of Washington University School of Medicine has also developed, under the leadership of Dr. E. F. Gildea, a study on the psychiatric aspects of aging. By careful evaluation of patient material, the goal of this research program is to minimize admission of older people to psychiatric hospitals.

Dr. Marion E. Bunch of the Department of Psychology of Washington University is also planning an extensive research program oriented toward the description of age changes in various types of performance. Although some of the studies will utilize laboratory techniques, major emphasis will be placed on developing performance tests that can be administered to large numbers of industrial workers. It is hoped the program can be maintained as a longitudinal study.

Dr. W. H. Reals of the Department of Adult Education has been particularly interested in the development of preretirement programs and other educational activities designed to maintain the health and activity of aging people. He is also planning courses to train laymen to carry on action programs for elderly people in their communities.

Institute of Gerontology, University of Iowa, Iowa City, Iowa.— In January 1953, the State Board of Education established the Institute of Gerontology at the University of Iowa. In September 1953, Dr. S. M. Horvath of the Department of Physiology of the College of Medicine was appointed acting director of the institute. The institute, which is directly under the president of the university, has, along with its director, two advisory committees. The membership of the Citizens Advisory Committee consists of 12 residents of Iowa, chosen because of their active interest in gerontology. The University Advisory Committee is composed of 13 faculty members who help the institute in its functioning as a university-wide organization. The institute receives funds from the university budget, which is appropriated by the state legislature. In addition to these funds, the institute accepts grants-in-aid for research programs. The main function of the institute is to provide a stimulus to other institutes and to various colleges and departments of the university to engage in research in the broadest aspects of gerontology. This function of the institute includes the organization of discussion groups, the support of personnel, and the actual transfer of funds to other departments of the university engaged in gerontological research. The institute offers limited financial support for graduate students. A small staff is maintained by the institute itself to engage in research and other activities. The goal of the institute is to initiate programs that other interested groups of the university can then take over.

The second function of the institute is to supply information and competent advice to communities engaged in building programs for the aged. This is accomplished, in part, through a monthly bulletin published by the institute and by conferences held both at the university and within communities in the state.

The institute also contributes to the university teaching program. Staff members give lectures which touch on gerontology in medical, liberal arts, commerce, and social work courses. It also offers a graduate course entitled "Basic Aspects of Gerontology," which utilizes the University Advisory Committee and other experts in their respective fields. This course offers three semester hours' credit. Another course entitled "Physiology of the Aging Process" is offered in the Department of Physiology of the College of Medicine to hospital residents, both medical and dental, and to graduate students in the biological sciences.

Thus, the institute is making a significant contribution in stimulating research and in offering informational and training services.

Institute of Gerontology, University of Florida, Gainesville, Florida.—In 1951, the Institute of Gerontology of the University of Florida sponsored the First Annual Southern Conference on Gerontology. The conference has become an annual program, which has considered such diverse problems as population changes, health, and retirement.[2] Dr. I. L. Webber is director of the institute. Most of the research conducted by members of the institute has been concerned primarily with sociological aspects of aging. These studies of communities, living arrangements, and migration of the elderly have been carried out within the specific departments of the university. Plans are presently under way to expand the scope of this institute to include representatives from the Medical School and the biological sciences. It is hoped that funds will be obtained which will permit the direct operation of research programs.

Division of Gerontology, Institute of Human Relations, University of Michigan, Ann Arbor, Michigan.—Although the Institute of Human Relations of the University of Michigan began its series of conferences on aging in 1948, the Division of Gerontology was not established until 1951. Dr. Wilma T. Donahue, who is chief of the division, has continued the program of annual conferences, which have served a very useful function in emphasizing various aspects of aging.[3] They have offered an opportunity for intensive instruction of individuals concerned with action programs and have stimulated research workers to speculate on the significance of their findings. In addition to the conference programs, the division has conducted surveys of communities and has investigated the effects of recreational programs in institutions for the aged. At Michigan the first course for preretirement education was developed, and through contacts with industry the importance of preretirement counseling has been highlighted. This group has been most active in developing training programs for workers in the field and in developing methods for organization of community facilities. Last year, the Gerontology Division was awarded a substantial grant from the Division of Research Grants of the National Institutes of Health to develop materials for training workers in the social science aspects of gerontology. This program will be carried out with the collaboration of eight other university groups and will be coordinated by Dr. Donahue.

In the Department of Psychology of the University of Michigan, Dr. E. L. Kelly has reported significant studies on age changes in personality characteristics. These studies were based on interviews and tests made on the same individuals (aged 35–45) after a 15-year interval. The results showed an increase in masculine attitudes, greater value placed on religion, and significant alterations in attitudes toward political parties, religious groups, and social movements.

Department of Gerontology, University of Kansas Medical School, Kansas City, Kansas.—The University of Kansas has established a Department of Gerontology within the Department of Medicine of the Medical School. The program is directed by Dr. E. H. Hashinger and is concerned primarily with clinical research on aged hospital patients. In addition, the department has organized a postgraduate course in geriatrics which is offered annually to physicians. The course consists of lectures and clinical demonstrations over a two-day period. In addition, members of the staff organize conferences among physicians within local communities in the state.

Moosehaven Laboratory, Orange Park, Florida.—In September 1949, a research laboratory was opened at Moosehaven. This laboratory was created and financed by the Moose fraternity as an extension of the support given to research by the Moose since the founding in 1930 of the Mooseheart Laboratory for Child Research. The purpose of the Moosehaven Laboratory is "the investigation of physical, nutritional, social, educational, and emotional factors contributing to the improvement and maintenance of health in the aging population." Dr. R. W. Kleemeier serves as director. The laboratory is located in special quarters constructed by the fraternity for research purposes. Special laboratories for psycho-physiological research are available to the staff. In addition to the permanent staff of four investigators, the laboratory has collaborated with the University of Florida and offers opportunities for graduate students to carry out their investigations at Moosehaven. The research program has been concerned with perceptual changes, psychomotor changes, intellectual performance, learning capacity, reaction time, and electroencephalographic responses with age. In addition, studies on social organization and on the effects of work programs on social adjustment have been carried out. The subjects used for these studies come from a population of some 350 men and women who are residents of Moosehaven, a retirement colony beautifully situated on the St. Johns River. The population, drawn from members of the Moose fraternity in all parts of the United States, is relatively stable, so that longitudinal studies are possible. This laboratory has great potentials for effecting longitudinal studies, and it is hoped that such activities can be expanded in the future.

Gerontology Branch, National Heart Institute, Baltimore City Hospitals, Baltimore, Maryland.—The Unit on Gerontology was officially established in the National Institutes of Health as part of the Division of Physiology in July 1940. It was supported during its first year by research grants from the Josiah Macy, Jr., Foundation. Dr. E. J. Stieglitz served as head of the unit, and through his efforts a cooperative arrangement with the Baltimore City Hospitals was effected for laboratory space in the Chronic Disease Hospital. In July 1941, the grant from the Macy Foundation expired and the full financial support of the program was assumed by the United States Public Health Service. At this time, Dr. Stieglitz returned to private medical practice and Dr. N. W. Shock, assistant professor of physiology at the University of California Medical School, was appointed chief of the unit. The budget of the unit was increased and a complete chemistry laboratory was established in space provided by the City Hospitals. Studies on the effects of aging on kidney function were initiated, but were dropped during the war years when the laboratory was engaged in research on the effect of vitamins of the B complex on work output and fatigue. In July 1946, through the active support of Dr. W. H. Sebrell, chief of the Division of Physiology, the budget was again increased and eight additional staff members were appointed. The Baltimore City Hospitals made available an entire wing of the Chronic Disease Hospital, which was remodeled to provide additional laboratory facilities.

With the establishment of the National Heart Institute in 1948, the activities of the Gerontology Section were transferred to this institute. Through the support of Dr. C. J. Van Slyke, who was then director of the Heart Institute, further increases in the budget made it possible to increase the staff to a total of 48. The Baltimore City Hospitals provided additional space, which was remodeled to provide approximately 10,000 square feet of laboratories. X-ray equipment, temperature-controlled rooms, and other specialized research equipment permitted expansion of the program. At the present time, the Gerontology Branch functions as one of the operating units of the Intramural Research Division (Dr. R. W. Berliner) of the National Heart Institute. Through the support of Dr. James Watt, Director of the National Heart Institute, it has been possible to add a section on basic biology to the program of the Gerontology Branch. The City Hospitals have made available additional space to permit the maintenance of experimental animals to advanced ages for this program.

In 1956, the National Institute of Mental Health joined with the Heart Institute in supporting an expanded program on the psychological aspects of aging. This program will deal primarily with studies on the relationships between physiological characteristics and performance capacities in the human. It will also develop contacts with organized groups in the Baltimore area to furnish subjects for other studies. Experimental investigations of mental performance, personality, and emotional characteristics, as well as social interrelationships, will be pursued.

Although the total program is a direct operation of the National Institutes of Health, it also receives substantial support from the Baltimore City Hospitals. Salaries for the full-time research staff, as well as the cost of equipment and operating expenses, are paid from the regular appropriations available to the National Institutes of Health. At the present time, the laboratory consists of 15 investigators, recruited from the disciplines of cellular physiology, enzyme chemistry, biochemistry, physiology, medicine, and psychology. The remainder of the staff of 35 is composed of chemists, biologists, technicians, secretaries, and computers, to aid in the research program. Members of the professional staff of the Gerontology Branch also hold visiting appointments on the staff of the Baltimore City Hospitals. The physicians participate in the general medical program of the hospital, thus assuring close collaboration between the two staffs. In addition, the laboratory facilities of the Branch are made available to qualified members of the house staff of the hospital for pursuing specific problems in clinical research. In addition to making patients in the City Hospitals and the Old People's Home available for study, the City Hospitals provide all services such as light, heat, water, gas, and electricity, as well as food, operating expenses, and nursing care for the patients.

The Baltimore City Hospitals have also placed one ward of 60 beds at the disposal of the Gerontology Branch for maintenance of patients under study. All new admissions to the Old People's Home are referred to this ward for medical evaluation and diagnosis. These patients are admitted for domiciliary care and not for medical reasons. They are carefully screened by members of the medical staff of the Gerontology Branch, and if they meet the requirements set up for any individual study, they are given the opportunity to participate. All of the 60 beds on this ward are reserved for research purposes, and admissions to these beds are under the control of the medical staff of the Gerontology Branch. In addition to the regular flow of new patients for domiciliary care, patients may be transferred from other wards of the hospital and from the Old People's Home (with a population of approximately 600 ambulatory guests) to these beds for experimental study. Since none of the beds are used for the care of chronic patients, they are always available for research problems.

The over-all research goals of the Gerontology Branch include the following: (a) basic biology of the aging process, (b) the changes with age in the environmental fluids of the body (plasma, extracellular, and intracellular components), (c) age changes in metabolic processes of cells and tissues, (d) the study of age changes and the reaction of body cells to alterations in composition of their environment, (e) alterations in the functional capacities of organs and organ systems with age, (f) age changes in the integrated responses of individuals, (g) the study of the development of aging phenomena in individual subjects by repeated observations on the same subject over a number of years, and (h) the psychological aspects of aging.

Research problems of the branch are organized under five major sections: (1) biology and cellular physiology of aging, (2) human physiology, (3) human performance, (4) psychological aspects, and (5) geriatrics. The section on biology and cellular physiology is investigating problems of age changes in enzyme activities of various tissues, mortality rates in lower species and the factors that influence them, age differences in synthesis of cellular proteins, and age differences in intermediary metabolism. These studies are being carried out on lower animal forms, as well as with the tissues of young and old rats. The section on human physiology is investigating the responsiveness of various organ systems to physiological stresses. Organ systems of particular interest are the cardiovascular system, the kidney, and the endocrine glands. The section on human performance is studying age differences in response to various types of standardized exercise. The goal of this program is to identify the factors involved in the reduction in speed and capacity for muscular work, or for coordinative tasks with increasing age. The section on psychology, which is supported jointly by the National Institute of Mental Health, is concerned with the relationship between physiological characteristics and emotional responses in older people. Intellectual performance and, particularly, the effects of sampling bias on test results are being investigated. Other studies include measurements of psychomotor ability and the application of objective methods to estimates of age changes in interests and attitudes. The unit on geriatrics utilizes patient material from all wards of the hospital for investigation of disease processes in older people.

The Gerontology Branch also collaborates with other laboratories; studies on vitamin B_{12} in the aged and studies on tissue enzymes have been carried out in collaboration with Dr. B. F. Chow of the School of Hygiene and Public Health, Johns Hopkins University. Similarly, Dr. Warren Andrew is carrying out histological investigations on tissues which have been analyzed for enzyme activities in the laboratories of the Gerontology Branch. A study on human performance represents a collaborative venture with Dr. R. W. Ramsey of the Medical College of Virginia.

During the past 15 years, over 200 papers have been published by the members of the staff of the Gerontology Branch. These reports range from studies on age changes in enzyme activities of various tissues to studies of age changes in mental performance.

Section on Aging, National Institute of Mental Health, Bethesda, Maryland.—In 1951, the National Institute of Mental Health established a Section on Aging within the Psychological Laboratory. Under the leadership of Dr. J. E. Birren, the section now includes a staff of seven professional scientists and ten technicians, plus supporting personnel. The research program of the section is organized into three operating units: (1) The unit on anatomy and histochemistry is studying submicroscopic changes in cells of the nervous system by means of both conventional microscopy and electron microscopy. (2) The unit on biochemistry and physiology is concerned with the assessment of biological properties of the aging nervous system. (These studies include estimates of enzyme activities of brain tissues, as well as quantitative analyses of brain constituents such as the electrolytes, lipids, proteins, and nucleic acids. The unit is also concerned with age differences in the action and metabolism of neuropharmaceutical agents.) (3) The unit on psychology is studying behavioral changes with age in both humans and rats. Current studies on humans include age changes in learning, flexibility of set, and time and intensity relations in perception. A special animal colony has been established for maintaining rats throughout their natural life span. In addition, Dr. Birren is coordinating a study of human aging which requires the cooperation of three laboratories in the National Institutes of Health and 12 different investigators. The object of the study is to correlate personality, cognitive, perceptual, and physiological factors in normally aging individuals. Over 40 procedures and tests are included in the observations, as, for example, cerebral metabolism and blood flow, psychiatric assessment, cognitive and perceptual functions, medical and ophthalmological examinations, social relationships, and assessment of personality characteristics. These studies are being conducted on elderly people living in the community who take up residence in the Clinical Center at Bethesda for a period of seven to ten days, during which time the tests are carried out. This laboratory has already made significant contributions to our knowledge about the psychological and behavioral aspects of aging and the structural and functional characteristics of the nervous system.

Although the primary focus of research on aging in the National Institutes of Health is in the Gerontology Branch of the National Heart Institute and the Section on Aging of the National Institute of Mental Health, individual investigators in other institutes are pursuing investigations directly related to gerontology. In 1956, there were seven such programs in the National Cancer Institute, three in the National Institute of Arthritis and Metabolic Diseases, three in the National Institute of Neurological Diseases and Blindness, and three in the National Institute of Dental Research. These projects included studies on age changes in joints, red blood cells, cancer morbidity, connective tissue, nervous system, cerebral blood flow, nutritional requirements, and dentition.

Institute of Gerontology, University of Miami, Miami, Florida.— The Institute of Gerontology has been established at the University of Miami under the leadership of Dr. Samuel Gertman. This institute is interested primarily in medical problems and has developed a training program in geriatrics. Major emphasis in research and in training is on the diseases of older people and methods for rehabilitation.

Dr. Gordon Ring, in the Physiology Department of the University of Miami, is also planning studies on aging. Drs. R. J. Boucek and N. L. Noble are investigating age changes in connective tissue.

LABORATORIES WITH CONTINUING INTEREST IN
AGING RESEARCH

Goldwater Memorial Hospital, Welfare Island, New York City.— Two research sections are in operation in the Goldwater Memorial Hospital of New York City. One of these is associated with Columbia University College of Physicians and Surgeons and the other with the New York University Medical School. The Columbia Division is under the direction of Dr. D. Segall and has a primary interest in renal physiology and the problems of arteriosclerosis. The second division, associated with the New York University Medical School, is under the direction of Dr. J. M. Steele. Both divisions have extensive laboratories and animal facilities available for research, and have made major contributions to our knowledge of arteriosclerosis, cardiovascular-renal diseases, and arthritis. Utilizing patient material available, these laboratories have also devised methods for determining age changes in body composition. Studies on rehabilitation of older patients are also being carried on at the Goldwater Memorial Hospital under the direction of Dr. M. M. Dacso. Both services offer valuable training to young physicians interested in geriatrics, chronic diseases, and rehabilitation.

Worcester Foundation, Shrewsbury, Massachusetts.— Dr. H. Hoagland and Dr. G. Pincus have carried out extensive studies on age changes in excretion of steroid hormones and responses to both physiological and psychological stress situations. The subjects consist of normal people from the community (members of the police force and fire department are included as volunteer subjects), augmented by mental patients from the Worcester State Hospital. This laboratory is investigating many of the basic problems of age changes in various endocrine systems.

College of Physicians and Surgeons, Columbia University, New York City.—Dr. H. S. Simms has continued his studies on aging in the rat and mouse. He has utilized an animal colony housed in a special building provided with air conditioning, uniform lighting, and other standardized conditions, aimed to minimize the effects of environment and infections on longevity of the animals. Animals have been carried from birth to death, and detailed autopsy reports have been made by Dr. Simms and Dr. B. N. Berg. As a result, these studies offer some of our best data on longevity and causes of death in the rat and mouse. At the present time, studies on a variety of physiological factors are being applied to this group of aging animals.

Dr. Simms has also continued his investigations on substances that he has isolated from blood serum, which both accelerate and retard the deposition of fat in the cells of tissue cultures. Dr. R. F. Loeb and Dr. G. A. Perera have continued their studies on the relationship of the adrenal cortex to hypertensive vascular disease. These investigators have shown that, in hypertensive disease, there is often an excretion of abnormal substances in the urine.

Dr. F. J. Kallmann is also continuing his studies on aging in twins. From his investigations on a large number of aged twins, Dr. Kallmann has been able to demonstrate similarities between the nature of disease processes and even the time of their occurrence in twins. Thus it seems that in the human as well as in lower forms heredity plays an important role in determining the rate of aging.

Cornell University, Ithaca, New York.—A good share of our knowledge about the relationships between diet and longevity has come from research studies carried out by Dr. C. M. McCay in the College of Agriculture of Cornell University. Financed by grants from the Rockefeller Foundation, these studies were initiated in 1927. Original investigations were carried out on brook trout but, in 1930, studies were shifted to the rat. For these studies, special air-conditioned quarters were built. Between 1939 and 1943, dogs were employed in his cooperative studies on behavior and learning, with Dr. H. S. Liddell of the Department of Psychology. During the war years, the work with dogs was terminated, but in 1947 Stockard Animal Farm was turned over to Dr. McCay and Dr. Liddell for additional studies with dogs. For this program, pure-bred dogs of varying ages were collected from animal breeders and have been maintained to the end of their life span. In addition, young animals were also bred for the purpose of longitudinal studies. Investigations on variations in diet, nutritional requirements, pathological changes in tissues, and the influence of exercise in animals at various ages have been made. As previously reported, the researches from this laboratory showed an increased longevity in rats which were maintained on diets adequate with respect to minerals and vitamins but containing only one-half the caloric intake consumed by litter mates. Up to the present, it has not been possible to demonstrate a similar effect among dogs. This is related, in part, to difficulty in maintaining young puppies completely free from gastrointestinal parasites. Other studies on the metabolism of the dog showed that calcium was lost more easily from the bodies of old dogs than from young. This laboratory has collaborated with investigators from other universities and institutions and has, for example, done extensive work on age changes in dentition.

Recently, Dr. McCay and his collaborators have developed a new technique for the study of aging. This technique involves the production of artificial Siamese twins; i.e., the surgical grafting of two animals together. They have been able to produce pairs of animals which differed by as much as 300 days in age. These studies, which are only preliminary in nature, should provide basic information on aging. The primary question is whether the attachment of animals of two different ages will result in rejuvenation of the older member of the pair, or more rapid senescence in the younger.

The Department of Sociology at Cornell University has also been active in sponsoring research on aging. Dr. G. F. Streib is studying the effects of retirement on personal adjustment, health, and longevity. Preliminary results fail to demonstrate the common belief that aging and death are often accelerated by retirement. These studies emphasize the wide individual differences in responses to retirement and the importance of preretirement planning. Dr. B. Kutner, also of the Department of Sociology, has directed the survey of older people in the Kip's Bay–Yorkville Health District in New York City.

University of Minnesota, Minneapolis, Minnesota.—Dr. M. B. Visscher is continuing his studies on the effects of diet and age on the chemical composition of the mouse. For these studies, an extensive mouse colony has been set up under standardized environmental conditions to provide a supply of aging animals. The laboratories are supported by the Department of Physiology of the university, with supplementary research grants.

An extensive program on the aging process in normal human beings is going forward under the direction of Dr. Ancel Keys of the Department of Physiological Hygiene. The department is housed beneath the spectator stands of the University Stadium where extensive laboratories and experimental rooms are available for various studies. One important aspect of the research program of this group is the longitudinal study of white-collar workers. In 1950, 300 males between the ages of 45 and 54 volunteered for a series of tests to be repeated annually. This group was selected from 800 volunteers for the program. At annual intervals, each subject reports to the laboratory without breakfast; he is given a physical examination, and a medical history is taken. Following this, blood samples are drawn for various chemical determinations. In addition to standard anthropometric measurements and blood pressure, a wide variety of laboratory tests are administered, as, for example, body composition, electrocardiogram, pulse wave velocity, and response to exercise. In addition, a battery of psychological tests and questionnaires on diet and physical activity is administered. This study is still in progress, with less than 10 percent loss of subjects to the sample. Although it is still too early to evaluate the extent to which certain measurements may indicate impending cardiovascular disease, this longitudinal study has already demonstrated its worth in showing that the reduction in blood cholesterol, which occurs at about the age of 50, is an individual characteristic, and cannot be attributed simply to the death of individuals with high levels. Continuation of this study, preferably until all members of the sample have died, represents one of our most valuable assets for gerontological research. We are also indebted to Dr. Keys and his associates for demonstrating the feasibility of securing for experimental purposes the cooperation of normal people living in the community.

Dr. Keys and Dr. H. L. Taylor are initiating another study to compare the effects of varying degrees of exercise on the health status of middle-aged males. For this study, they propose to make a series of tests on railroad workers, comparing railroad yard workers with sedentary workers. A mobile laboratory, set up in a railroad baggage car, will make it possible to conduct tests on workers in their normal environment. This study will be of primary importance in assessing the effects of physical activity on physiological status and longevity.

University of Chicago, Chicago, Illinois.—The Committee on Human Development, under the chairmanship of Dr. R. J. Havighurst, has had a continuing interest in the sociological aspects of aging. The questionnaire, designed by Dr. Havighurst, Dr. E. W. Burgess, Dr. R. S. Cavan, and Dr. H. Goldhamer, to estimate the social adjustment of older people has been widely applied by many other investigators.[4] The survey of a small midwestern community has done much to dispel the belief that all older people are necessarily maladjusted invalids.[5] Similarly, the analysis of the meaning of work and retirement has done much to clarify our concepts and has shown the importance of these variables in determining adjustment to retirement.[6]

In Kansas City the Committee on Human Development is also concerned with an extensive community study of aging. This study of a stratified sample of 1,000 men and women, aged 40 to 70 years, utilizes the interview technique. Five different interviews, concerned with personal and social development, have been conducted on samples of 200 selected cases. The interview material is examined and ratings are made for performance in the major role areas for adults, such as parent, spouse, adult child of aging parents, homemaker, worker, user of leisure time, church member, club or association member, citizen, friend.[7]

A collaborative study involving the Committee for Human Development, the Institute of Industrial Relations, the Department of Medicine, and the Department of Psychology is also in progress. This study is being conducted on middle-aged and older executives to determine age changes in performance, health status, and personality characteristics. Subjects are admitted to the Billings Hospital for medical and physiological evaluation by Dr. E. B. Bay and his staff. Psychological tests are administered by Dr. W. C. Halstead, and sociological evaluations are made by other staff members.

The Institute of Industrial Relations, under the direction of Dr. R. K. Burns, has been active in promoting the use of preretirement programs in industry. The institute is also collaborating with the Committee on Human Development and the Moosehaven Laboratory in investigations on living arrangements and social adjustment among retired workers. One study has been concerned with social relationships in a trailer camp in Florida.

The National Opinion Research Center of the University of Chicago is at present conducting a national survey on the health problems of older people under a grant from the Health Information Foundation. The aim is to determine how a national sample of older people perceive their own health problems, and how persons close to them regard these problems and needs. The study is under the direction of Dr. Ethel Shanas and Dr. James Colemen.

Bowman Gray School of Medicine, Winston-Salem, North Carolina.—The numerous studies of Dr. Warren Andrew on the age changes in the structural characteristics of tissues and cells have long been classics in the field. With expanded laboratory facilities available at the Bowman Gray School of Medicine, Dr. Andrew and Dr. N. M. Sulkin are planning an expansion of these programs, with the possible addition of training programs as well. Dr. Andrew is particularly interested in correlating structural changes in tissues and cells with their physiological characteristics.

University of Louisville, Louisville, Kentucky.—Dr. James B.

Rogers has developed one of the few colonies of aged guinea pigs in the United States. He has been interested in the anatomical changes which occur in various organs, particularly the kidney, in these animals of advanced ages. He has also reported studies on age changes in blood chemistry in these animals and has furnished tissues to other investigators for their studies. Although the average life span of the guinea pig is approximately two to three years, Dr. Rogers has been able to maintain some animals as long as eight years. All animals have been autopsied at death and tissues have been preserved for histological examination.

University of Pittsburgh, Pittsburgh, Pennsylvania.—Dr. A. I. Lansing has recently been appointed chairman of the Department of Anatomy at the University of Pittsburgh. He is planning the expansion of his research program on the basic biological aspects of aging, utilizing a variety of animal species. These studies will be concerned with both the functional and structural characteristics of tissues and cells from older animals. In the Psychology Department of the university, Dr. H. W. Braun has initiated a program of research on the psychological aspects of aging. He is particularly interested in limitations in the rate of learning. The School of Public Health, under the direction of Dr. T. Parran, has also been interested in the effects of environmental factors on aging. Dr. H. S. Belding is conducting a study on the effects of age on the ability to work. The health status of the aged and the organization of community services for older people have also been studied in the School of Public Health.

Home for Aged and Infirm Hebrews, New York City.—In addition to its outstanding program of services, the Home for Aged and Infirm Hebrews, under the leadership of Dr. F. D. Zeman, also engages in research. The research program includes investigations on age changes in carbohydrate metabolism, studies on histological and structural changes of the eye with aging, the influence of various types of activity programs on social adjustment in the elderly, and age changes in personality characteristics. Perhaps the greatest contribution of the home has been the demonstration of effective rehabilitation programs for elderly hemiplegic patients.

Home and Hospital for the Daughters of Jacob, New York City.—

In 1954, the Home and Hospital for the Daughters of Jacob established an Institute of Geriatrics for research on the diseases of the aged. Clinical research studies, with particular emphasis on nutrition and the effects of vitamin supplements, are being pursued. These programs, initiated by the late Dr. H. A. Rafsky, are being supervised by Dr. B. F. Chow.

Duke University, Durham, North Carolina.—In 1955, Duke University established a Council on Gerontology under the chairmanship of Dr. E. W. Busse, chairman of the Department of Psychiatry. The council includes members of the Departments of Psychology, Sociology, Anatomy, Biochemistry, Education, Economics, Law, Urosurgery, Obstetrics and Gynecology, Pathology, Pastoral Care, Physical Education, and Nursing. The function of the council is to stimulate interest in research in gerontology at Duke University, to exchange information, and to facilitate research in gerontology by assisting in securing funds for education, research, publications, scholarships, and fellowships. The program is broadly conceived and places major emphasis on interdisciplinary research. Although this program is still in formative stages, there are a number of research studies in operation at the present time. For example, Dr. Busse is continuing work initiated at the University of Denver on the effects of aging on the central nervous system. These studies are attempting to correlate physiological, psychological, and personality characteristics of aging individuals. The present research staff is drawn from the following fields of interest: psychiatry, psychology, general medicine, cardiology, anatomy, ophthalmology, gerontology, electroencephalography, neurology, social anthropology, and social work. The older people studied have been volunteers from various community groups such as Golden Age Club members and their families and friends, older physicians, and retired college professors, as well as patients at general and mental hospitals. All subjects are 60 years of age or older. Populations in North Carolina are being selected so that they will be comparable with those studied in Colorado. Other studies on age changes in senile cerebral disease are in progress in the Department of Pathology.

University of California, Berkeley, California.—At the University of California, Dr. Harold E. Jones, Department of Psychology, and Dr. Hardin B. Jones, Donner Laboratory, are conducting psychological and physiological examinations on a group of male and female subjects, aged 30 to 35 years. These subjects were drawn from those used in the study of adolescence carried out by the Institute of Child Welfare (Dr. Harold E. Jones, director) in 1932–40. In this original study, each person, 10 or 11 years old in 1932, was examined at semi-annual intervals up to the age of 18. In the current study, a battery of physiological and psychological tests was administered. Of the total sample of 100 subjects (50 males and 50 females), approximately 85 were still available for testing. Although the data have not been completely analyzed, preliminary results indicate that, over this age span, there is a tendency for an increase in performance on mental tests rather than a decrease. Since many of the physiological measurements made on these subjects as children were repeated (blood pressure, basal metabolism, and responses to standard exercises), it will be possible to assess the stability of some of these functions as well. It is hoped that this valuable group of subjects can be given repeated examinations at five-year intervals throughout their life span.

Other departments of the University of California have also been interested in specific aspects of aging. Thus, in the Biochemistry Department, Dr. D. M. Greenberg has studied age differences in some enzyme activities of rat liver, and Dr. I. L. Chaikoff has made significant contributions to our knowledge about age changes in lipid metabolism. The Institute of Industrial Relations at the University of California has also carried out studies on the development of criteria for continued employment among workers. In these studies, both physiological and psychological tests have been applied.

Cedars of Lebanon Hospital, Los Angeles, California.—Dr. H. Sobel and Dr. J. Marmorston have been investigating the problems of age changes in tissue characteristics. Important contributions to our knowledge of the physiology of connective tissue, which plays an important role in the aging of many organs, have been made. In 1955, the Ciba Foundation awarded one of its prizes for research in gerontology to Dr. Sobel and Dr. Marmorston for this work. On the basis of these studies, it is proposed that aging is conditioned by the quantity of gel relative to the quantity of fiber that is laid down in connective tissue. Since cells receive their nutrients and products of metabolism are removed by transfers through the extracellular environment which contains connective tissue, the relative increase in the quantity of fiber, with increasing age, results in an impairment in the transfer of materials to and from each living cell. These workers have also made important contributions to our knowledge about the age changes in the excretion of various hormones.

Syracuse University, Syracuse, New York.—Dr. R. G. Kuhlen of the Department of Psychology has been interested in the psychological aspects of aging for a number of years. He has made important contributions with regard to personality changes with age. Recently, Dr. V. J. Wulff of the Department of Zoology has initiated a program of research on the basic biology of aging. One project is concerned with age changes in enzyme activities of mitochondria separated from the nervous system of rats of increasing age. Other studies in the department include the effects of aging on the responses of tissues and cells to the administration of various hormones.

New York University College of Medicine, New York City.—Dr. M. Rockstein is studying aging in flies and rats. His studies on flies are directed primarily toward the effects of parental age on longevity. In addition, he plans to study age changes in various enzyme systems in the flies. Similar observations on age changes in enzyme activities will be made on tissues of old and young rats.

Galesburg State Research Hospital, Galesburg, Illinois.—Dr. H. E. Himwich and Wilhelmina A. Himwich are conducting experiments on age changes in enzyme activity and chemical composition of the nervous system. This laboratory is supported by the State of Illinois. Excellent laboratory facilities are available for basic research. At the present time, rabbits are being used for experimental material. Although Dr. Himwich has been successful in securing a substantial number of pedigreed old rabbits, he plans to establish a colony which will give data on the life expectancy of rabbits as well as provide controlled experimental material.

Yale University, New Haven, Connecticut.—Dr. J. A. Parfentjev is conducting studies on age changes in plasma proteins and alterations in immunity. The basic studies utilize rats and mice as experimental material.

Dorn Laboratory for Medical Research, Bradford, Pennsylvania. —This laboratory, under the direction of Dr. A. Dury, has been interested in age changes in the vascular system with special reference to the relationship of endocrine factors to the development of arteriosclerosis. A survey of age changes in chemical and enzyme characteristics of blood vessels is being sponsored by this laboratory.

Western Reserve University, Cleveland, Ohio.—Dr. G. L. Freeman has been carrying on a study of interests and attitudes among preretirees. Recently, a basic science laboratory has been set up by Dr. A. B. Chinn. This laboratory, located in the Benjamin Rose Hospital, is carrying on investigations on age differences in protein structure with particular reference to connective tissue.

The Highland View Hospital in Cleveland is conducting a study of the vocational potentials of patients hospitalized with severe chronic disabilities.

The Benjamin Rose Institute of Cleveland is continuing its program on the effects of activity programs on social adjustment and health of the aged.

Fels Institute, Yellow Springs, Ohio.—The Fels Institute, under the direction of Dr. L. W. Sontag, has been carrying out a longitudinal study among children and their parents. The measurements include autonomic responses to various types of stimuli, personality characteristics, blood lipid changes, and alterations in body composition. Adjustments required in three-generation families are being investigated. This research institute, housed in its own building with some 90 experimental rooms, in the past has been primarily interested in growth and development. A number of longitudinal studies on children have been carried out, and it is gratifying to see the extension of these programs to include the entire field of gerontology.

Roswell Park Memorial Institute, Springville, New York.—Dr. L. C. Strong has, for many years studied the genetic aspects of cancer in mice. Limitations of space have thus far made it impossible for him to maintain these animals throughout their life span. However, Dr.

Strong is interested in the genetic aspects of longevity in mice, and is planning an extension of his program in this direction.

University of Buffalo, Buffalo, New York.—In May 1950, the University of Buffalo established a Chronic Disease Research Institute. Dr. S. Rodbard has initiated studies on the etiology and prevention of diseases of later life, with particular emphasis on arteriosclerosis. In addition, Dr. A. W. Brody in the Department of Anatomy is studying structural changes in the nervous system of aged rats and humans. He is particularly interested in determining the factors concerned with the observed reduction in the number of nerve cells with advancing age.

University of Connecticut, Storrs, Connecticut.—Dr. E. P. Jayne in the Department of Anatomy is continuing his studies on structural changes in tissues and cells with age. In the Department of Sociology, Dr. W. C. McKain, Jr., is continuing his studies on social adjustment of rural people to retirement. This represents one of the relatively few research programs concerned with aging in rural populations. The University of Connecticut has under consideration expansion of this research program.

Columbia University, New York City.—Dr. Irving Lorge has made significant contributions to our knowledge of age changes in intellectual performance. In addition, the attitudes of workers and employees toward older workers have been reported. These programs represent a continuing activity of this department.

Ohio State University, Columbus, Ohio.—Dr. S. L. Pressey of the Psychology Department has investigated the adjustment of older people to work and retirement. His studies have concentrated on the characteristics of successfully adjusted older people with identification of activities which are particularly adapted to aging individuals.

Dartmouth College, Hanover, New Hampshire.—Dr. S. M. Tenney has recently initiated a program for studies of age changes in respiratory physiology of the human.

Creedmore Institute for Psycho-Biologic Studies, Queens Village, New York.—This institute has a number of studies in progress dealing with both physiological and psychological aspects of aging in the human, with particular reference to interrelationships. One specific study is concerned with the terminal fragility of red cells from aged individuals. Other studies deal with the relationships between physiological variables and age changes in behavior and personality characteristics.

University of Utah, Salt Lake City, Utah.—Dr. L. T. Samuels is studying age changes in blood levels of various hormones. These studies are oriented primarily toward changes in the functional activity of the adrenal cortex. The University of Utah is also engaged in a long-term study of the effects of radiation on dogs. This colony of animals has great potential for the study of aging in the control animals, which are not subjected to radiation.

University of Oregon, Eugene, Oregon.—Dr. A. L. Soderwall is continuing his studies on changes in structural characteristics of tissues and cells.

Illinois Public Aid Commission, Chicago and Peoria, Illinois.— In collaboration with the Forest Park Foundation, Peoria, Illinois, the Illinois Public Aid Commission is carrying out an extensive study of rehabilitation among elderly people. In this program, the results of rehabilitation are being carefully evaluated by experimental procedures. In addition, rehabilitation programs are being organized in selected nursing homes, with special emphasis on training of workers. The goal of this program is to develop methods to decrease the institutionalization of the aged through improved procedures of diagnosis and rehabilitation. Of special importance is the design of this experiment to evaluate objectively the results of rehabilitation programs.

Purdue University, Lafayette, Indiana.—Dr. Herbert Hunsaker of the Department of Adult Education has organized a community study in a medium-sized city in Indiana. This program will investigate the psychological and sociological aspects of aging in individuals living in the community. Local committees have already been organized and various departments of the university are cooperating in formulating specific research programs. One study will be concerned with the factors that determine attitudes of older people toward aging, as well as the general community attitudes toward aging people. This program is planned to evaluate the effects of specific programs on estimates of attitudes. In addition, these studies will serve to demonstrate the possibility of using a total community for sociological and psychological research. The Department of Agricultural Economics at Purdue has also been interested in estimating energy requirements for a variety of farm operations. For this purpose, field studies have been carried out on Indiana farmers and, although primary emphasis has been placed on the effects of cardiovascular disease on performance, the control groups include individuals of different ages.

Brooklyn Home and Hospital for Aged and Infirm Hebrews, Brooklyn, New York.—Dr. Leo Gitman has organized an effective geriatric center at the Brooklyn Home and Hospital for Aged and Infirm Hebrews. In addition to the program of care, the home and hospital sponsor clinical research studies concerned with investigations on arteriosclerosis, the endocrine aspects of aging, and the etiology of arthritis. In addition to the home and hospital, a domiciliary residence is maintained for older people at Coney Island. This group of ambulatory elderly people is available for study, as well as a large population of older people living in the community who come into the residence for daily recreational activities. Dr. Gitman also contemplates the establishment of a laboratory for investigations on the basic biology of aging, using various animal species. These laboratories will be housed in a special wing which is now being added to the hospital.

Age Center of New England, Boston, Massachusetts.—With financial support from a number of industries in the Boston area, the Age Center of New England has organized a program for preretirement training, counseling, and recreational activities of older people. This center is contemplating a research program on the psychological and personality characteristics of older people, utilizing those who come to the center for a variety of services. The aim of the center, under the direction of Mr. Hugh Cabot, is the establishment of an accurate measure which will help business and industry to deal more effectively with both preretired and retiring workers. It is hoped to develop a reliable technique for predicting (1) the degree to which workers will be upset by the advance of years and approaching retirement, (2) whether, if an upset occurs, it will take a behavioral, psychological, or physical form, and (3) what factors could prevent or lessen the upset.

Lankenau Hospital, Philadelphia, Pennsylvania.—The Lankenau Hospital and Research Institute have, in the past, been primarily interested in cancer research. However, a number of studies, pertinent to aging, have been initiated. A study on the effects of exercise on deposition of cholesterol in the blood vessels of rabbits has already been carried out by Dr. E. L. Bortz in collaboration with Dr. C. M. McCay's laboratory at Cornell University. In addition, studies on basic enzyme chemistry are being considered by investigators at the Lankenau Research Institute.

Radiation and aging.—Interest in the effects of radiation on longevity has resulted in increasing our knowledge of gerontology. Thus, for example, Argonne, Brookhaven, and Oak Ridge laboratories are investigating problems concerned with the effects of low levels of radiation on total life span in mice and rats. The control groups from these studies offer basic data on aging in these species. A study has recently been instituted at the University of Wisconsin under the leadership of Dr. H. F. Harlow which will carry out longitudinal studies on monkeys. Although the primary goal of this investigation is to identify the effects of radiation, the control groups of monkeys will be a valuable asset for future gerontological research. Similarly, the studies carried out by the Atomic Bomb Casualty Commission on survivors in Hiroshima and Nagasaki will require, for the interpretation, comparable data on individuals from these populations who were not exposed to radiation. Since this study is longitudinal in its character, the addition of control groups would offer additional data for studies on aging in the human.

LABORATORIES IN FOREIGN COUNTRIES

Great Britain.—Dr. V. Korenchevsky has conducted research on the endocrine aspects of aging, utilizing the rat, for the past 20 years. These studies, originally located in the Department of Zoology, Oxford University, have been transferred to the Whittington Hospital in London. Dr. Korenchevsky's interest has been primarily on the histological changes induced in various organ systems in aged animals, following the administration of endocrine products. He has shown that, although certain aspects of aging may be retarded by the administration of hormones, there are potential hazards in these procedures. At Cambridge University, Dr. R. A. McCance has studied the responses of old and young men to starvation. Also at Cambridge, Dr. A. T. Welford and his staff have continued their investigations on psychological aspects of aging. Particular emphasis has been placed on the measurement and analysis of human skills and the effectiveness of retraining programs for industrial placement. Dr. O. Olbrich is in charge of a group of hospitals in Sunderland, England, and has developed an effective program of medical care for elderly people. In addition, Dr. Olbrich has made important contributions to our knowledge of age changes in blood chemistry and renal function and of changes in the cardiovascular system with age. At Wolverhampton, Dr. J. H. Sheldon, who served as president of the Third International Gerontological Congress, has continued his studies on the health status of older people. Similar studies of the health of older people living at home have been carried out in Sheffield by Dr. J. Pemberton. In Leeds, Dr. R. E. Tunbridge and his coworkers have an extensive research program on age changes in connective tissue. Dr. H. Droller, also of Leeds, has analyzed the incidence of falls and accidents in the aged. Mr. C. E. Fleming of the Department of Social and Industrial Medicine at the University of Sheffield has conducted important surveys of the age structure of workers in a variety of industries in Great Britain. At the University of Liverpool, Dr. D. B. Bromley has experimentally investigated the effects of age on creative intellectual output. Age differences in the reproductive physiology of primates are being investigated by Dr. P. Krohn at Birmingham University. Dr. L. Z. Cosin of Oxford Group Hospitals is engaged in research on the problem of rehabilitation and the organization of community services for care of the aged. At the Middlesex Hospital, Dr. Marjory W. Warren has done pioneer work in the rehabilitation of elderly hemiplegic patients.

In London, Dr. A. Comfort of the Department of Zoology of the University of London is engaged under a grant from the Nuffield Foundation in studies on the basic biology of aging. These studies are attempting to identify conditions which influence the life span of a number of lower organisms such as fish and Drosophila. Studies on the effects of parental age on longevity are also in progress. Dr. Comfort is particularly interested in comparing mortality curves of different species of animals. Dr. G. H. Bourne of the London Hospital Medical College is investigating age changes in the structural characteristics of various tissues, utilizing cytological and histochemical techniques. Dr. J. F. Danielli at King's College is developing techniques for the study of senescence in unicellular organisms such as amoebae.

St. Johns Hospital in London is concerned with the care of chronically ill patients, many of whom are elderly. Dr. T. H. Howell, who is in charge of the medical services, is carrying on a research program with particular emphasis on arteries and diseases of joints. In addition, autopsy material from older people has been analyzed by Dr. Howell. Dr. Howell was one of the pioneers in developing the "Half-Way House." This institution was established with nursing services to permit the care of patients who were not ill enough to occupy beds in the acute hospital but were still unable to care for themselves, either in their own homes or in domiciliaries. Lord Amulree has developed a most effective rehabilitation program in the St. Pancras Hospital in London. He has found that many elderly bedridden patients can, with adequate medical and nursing care, be rehabilitated to the point where they can lead successful lives under conditions of domiciliary care or in private homes.

Ireland.—Dr. J. F. Fleetwood of Dublin is engaged in clinical research of elderly patients, with particular reference to changes in red blood cells and hematology.

Belgium.—In Belgium, the major interest in gerontological and geriatric research is in the Department of Medicine of Liége University, under the leadership of Dr. L. Brull. This laboratory is engaged not only in clinical research on the diseases of older people, but has also made significant contributions in biochemistry and physiology. The program is very broad, including study of age differences in the response of various organ systems to physiological stresses and age differences in the chemical composition of tissues in the mouse.

France.—Dr. F. Bourlière of the Laboratory of Biology, Faculty of Medicine, Paris, is interested in the comparative physiology of aging. In addition to animal studies, Dr. Bourlière has collaborated with other departments of the Medical School in studies on humans, with measurements of metabolism, neurophysiology, etc. In 1956, the Seine County Council made available to Dr. Bourliére funds for the establishment of a research unit for the study of aging in normal people. Arrangements have been made with a large manufacturing firm whereby workers between the ages of 20 and 65, as well as retirees as old as 80, come to the research unit for a series of physiological and psychological tests at annual intervals. It is planned to continue the measurements in the same individual over a long period of years. In collaboration with Dr. L. Binet of the Department of Physiology, Dr. Bourlière has written an important volume entitled *Précis de Gerontologie* which summarizes much of the current knowledge about gerontology and geriatrics.[8] Dr. J. A. Huet of Paris has reported effects of age on the concentration of protein particles in blood plasma. He is also interested in the socioeconomic aspects of aging. Dr. J. Daric of Paris has been particularly interested in analyzing the age structure of the French population. Dr. R. Herbeuval is head of the Geriatric Department of the University of Nancy and has investigated problems of age changes in blood volume, fluid spaces, plasma proteins, and plasma electrolytes in aging humans.

Denmark.—Dr. T. Geill is chief of Old People's Town in Copenhagen, Denmark, and has investigated many clinical problems in elderly patients. This hospital has associated with it a large population under domiciliary care, so that many patients are available for study. Interest of this research group has been primarily in the field of cardiovascular physiology, nutrition, and problems of blood coagulation. Dr. C. Hamburger of the State Serum Institute in Copenhagen also made important contributions to our knowledge about the excretion of various hormones in older people. Dr. S. Eckerström, in collaboration with Dr. Geill, has published, in Danish, an important text in geriatrics.[9]

Finland.—Dr Eeva Jalavisto of the University of Helsinki has studied the effects of parental age on longevity by analyzing genealogical records from Scandinavia's noble families. Dr. Anitra Karsten has investigated some of the psychological and personality characteristics of older people, and Dr. T. Niemi is studying age differences in the response to exercise.

Germany.—Dr. M. Bürger of Leipzig has been a pioneer in studies on aging. He has, for many years, served as editor of the *Zeitschrift für Altersforschung* and has published an important textbook in gerontology and geriatrics.[10] Studies from this laboratory have covered a wide range of topics concerned primarily with the physiological characteristics of aging in the human.

Hungary.—In Budapest, Dr. I. Banga, Dr. J. Baló, and Dr. D. Szabó are investigating age changes in elastic fibers of connective tissue. Dr. E. Bajnsz is also engaged in age changes in the work capacity of specific muscles. Dr. L. Haranghy is carrying on histological studies on age changes in the spleen and blood-forming organs in the human.

Switzerland.—In Zürich, Dr. A. von Albertini has been interested in the structural changes in tissues with age, with particular reference to the problem of arteriosclerosis. In Basel, Dr. A. L. Vischer has been concerned with problems of rehabilitation and care of elderly patients. At the Physiological Institute of the University of Basel, Dr. F. Verzár and his wife have been conducting important investigations on the physiological and psychological aspects of aging. The Verzárs had developed a rat colony to provide them with aged animals for these studies. Dr. Verzár conducted important studies on age differences in compensatory hypertrophy of the kidney and the adrenal gland, as well as on differences in the adaptation to various environmental stresses such as high altitude and lowered temperature. His wife, Jean E. Verzár, has conducted psychological studies to determine age differences in the learning capacity of rats from this colony. They are now organizing a gerontological research unit which is located in the Department of Anatomy, University of Basel. Dr. Verzár, with Dr. R. Brüchner and Professor O. Gsell, has also organized a longitudinal study of aging in a group of young employees of the Ciba Company in Basel. At present, a series of physiological tests and medical examinations is being made on each subject at biannual intervals. It is planned to continue this study over the life span of the subjects who are now in their twenties and thirties.

Austria.—In Vienna, Dr. W. Doberauer and Dr. H. Hoff are studying the physiological characteristics of patients suffering from senile diseases, with particular reference to diseases of the nervous system.

Sweden.—Dr. S. Eckerström of Göteborg is engaged in research on clinical problems of elderly patients. He is particularly interested in nutritional problems and the factors that determine urinary incontinence in older people. Dr. H. Sjogren of Göteborg is interested in research on the psychiatric aspects of aging.

Netherlands.—The Netherlands Cancer Institute of Amsterdam, directed by Dr. O. Mühlbock, has available a large animal colony of mice which has been utilized for studies on cancer. Recently, Dr. Mühlbock and Dr. P. J. Thung have initiated a series of studies of age changes in these animals and the effects of genetic factors on longevity. Preliminary investigations have already been made on structural alterations in the sex organs of old mice, and additional physiological studies are contemplated. Also in Amsterdam, Dr. L. Van der Horst from the Psychiatric and Neurological Clinic of the Wilhelmina Hospital has been studying the neurological and psychiatric aspects of aging among his patients. Dr. R. J. van Zonneveld has organized a comprehensive survey of the health status of older people in the Netherlands. This study utilizes the services of a great many physicians in all parts of the Netherlands who are examining, in detail, a large percentage of the population over the age of 65. The physical examination has been worked out in detail, and Dr. van Zonneveld has set up briefing sessions with participating physicians in order to assure comparability between examinations made by different physicians. This health survey is unique in that it will be conducted by practicing physicians in all parts of the country.

Spain.—In 1946, the chair of geriatrics was founded by the Higher Council for Scientific Research in the Valencia University. The position has been occupied by Dr. M. Beltran Baguena who has been carrying out a research program on the factors involved in experimental atherosclerosis in rabbits. These studies have involved the structural analysis of blood vessels from these animals as well as chemical studies on blood lipoproteins. In addition, clinical research on patients in the hospital has been conducted. Dr. Beltran Baguena is also author of the first textbook of geriatrics published in Spanish.[11] Dr. F. Vega Díaz is director of the Department of Geriatrics of the Madrid General Hospital. This department is conducting investigations in cardiology and endocrinology in elderly patients. In Barcelona, Dr. M. Panella Casas has conducted important investigations on age changes in the skeletal system of the human. Radiographic techniques have been utilized for these studies.

Rumania.—Between 1930 and 1938, the Rumanian Institute for Investigations on Aging was directed by Dr. D. A. Kotsovsky. Over this period of time, the institute issued some 40 publications on various aspects of aging. During the war years, the operations of the institute were discontinued and Dr. Kotsovsky emigrated to Germany at the close of the war. Recently, the institute has been reactivated under the directorship of Dr. C. I. Parhon. The present interest of the institute is in the development of extracts of various tissues, including endocrine organs, for administration to aging individuals to improve their health status.

Italy.—Dr. E. Greppi, who served as president of the Fourth International Gerontological Congress in Italy in 1957, has been studying the physiological characteristics of older patients, with particular reference to senile arteriosclerosis. In these studies with Dr. F. M. Antonini, the variation in lipoproteins of the blood plasma, with age, and arteriosclerosis have been investigated. In Milan, Dr. G. Mars has been conducting studies on lung pathology in patients of advanced ages. Dr. Mars also serves as editor of *Giornale di Gerontologia,* published in Florence, Italy. In Rome, Dr. P. Alessandrini and Dr. N. Pende have also been interested in some of the clinical problems of older people.

Canada.—Dr. F. Bohatirchuk of Ottawa is conducting studies on aging in the human skeleton, utilizing radiographic techniques. At McGill University, a gerontological unit has been in operation in the Department of Psychiatry under the direction of Dr. D. E. Cameron since 1950. This unit has conducted studies on the psychiatric characteristics and sociological adjustment of older people, as well as bio-chemical studies both on patients and on animals. Dr. B. Grad is par-ticularly interested in the responses of aging rats to a variety of en-vironmental stresses such as alterations in temperature. Dr. Hans Selye of Montreal University has applied his concepts of the general adaptation syndrome to the aging process. The research program of this laboratory is extremely broad and contains a number of facets of interest to gerontologists, particularly studies on the tissue responses to the administration of various endocrine substances.

The Department of Veterans Affairs, Ottawa, is conducting stud-ies to establish objective criteria for retirement among industrial work-ers. Tests of physiological status are being developed.

Mexico.—In Mexico, Dr. M. Payno and Dr. J. Meneses Hoyos have been interested in clinical studies on aging patients. These stud-ies have been concerned chiefly with alterations in the cardiovascular system, with special reference to the electrocardiogram and the ballis-tocardiogram.

Summary.—This list of research laboratories and investigators, with continued interest in studies on aging, has shown a marked in-crease over those identified in 1950. As indicated, the greatest in-crease has been in the areas of studies on the biochemistry of aging and of studies dealing with psychological and sociological problems. There is no question but what substantial progress has been made over the past five years, and aging as an area for research is more highly regarded among investigators than has ever been true in the past. Although there has been a substantial increase in the number of investigators working on aging, many more are needed if we are to keep pace with current demands for information.

11

RECOMMENDATIONS: AN INSTITUTE OF GERONTOLOGY

Although many significant contributions to our knowledge about aging will continue to be made by individual investigators working in universities, hospitals, and government laboratories, it is clear that, because of the complexity and importance of the problems in gerontology, the organization of research institutes devoted specifically to gerontology will be required. Such an institute will give opportunity for daily contacts between workers in many scientific disciplines and will encourage coordinated programs in which the techniques of many different fields of science can be applied simultaneously to the same subject material. There are areas of responsibility in the field of gerontology, particularly in sociology and community programs, which are at present inadequately met and which should be associated with a comprehensive institute program. What, then, are the functions to be fulfilled by an Institute of Gerontology?

RESEARCH

One of the major functions of an Institute of Gerontology should be the fostering and execution of research programs on aging. These programs fall into four major categories: (1) the general biology of aging, (2) the physiological and psychological aspects of aging in man, (3) the clinical problems of aging man, and (4) the socioeconomic problems of an aging population.

The general biology of aging.—Studies on the aging process at the cellular level will require the use of animals other than man. The institute should therefore be provided with adequate facilities for rearing and maintaining unicellular organisms, insects, amphibia, mice, hamsters, rats, guinea pigs, rabbits, dogs, cats, and so on. Such studies include problems in genetics, the physical and chemical properties of protoplasm, enzyme chemistry, biochemistry, physiology, histology, and pathology. Facilities for rearing and maintaining animals under standardized conditions of environment, diet, heredity, and the like will of course be essential.

Physiological and psychological aspects of aging man.—Problems relating to the physiological, biochemical, and psychological aspects of aging man must be contemplated. Many of these studies will require long-term observations, beginning as early as the age of 20 and continuing throughout the life span in the same individuals. Sampling will be of extreme importance in the interpretation of results from such studies. Consequently, programs must be developed whereby both closely definable as well as random samples of the normal population can be studied. This means that cooperative arrangements must be made for normal, productive, successful people living in the community to be brought into the institute for testing purposes. For successful operation, a program involving the testing of normal elderly people will need to offer services of one kind or another. An institute adequately conceived and planned will provide service facilities for this purpose.

The research approach to the problems of aging man must be both analytical and integrative. In addition to studies on the functional capacities of different organ systems and their interrelations, provision must be made for over-all evaluations of performance. An important aspect of these studies will be the design of experiments to test reserve capacities of different organ systems by the application of definable physiological and psychological stresses with adequate measures of the rate of response and recovery. Physiologists, biochemists, and psychologists will need to collaborate in many of these experiments.

Clinical problems of aging man.—Although a great deal of research on the degenerative diseases of old age can be carried out within the framework of existing hospitals and medical schools, all of such studies suffer from the lack of knowledge about the patient prior to the beginning of the disease. Long-term studies planned as part of the institute program would offer the possibility of background information on the physiology, biochemistry, and psychology of the individual prior to the development of his disease. Thus, for the full utilization of the potentialities of the research institute, there should be some association with a hospital section where the clinical studies could be effectively pursued.

Socioeconomic problems. — While studies of population trends, mortality rates, economic status, and needs of elderly people might be carried out independently, coordination into an over-all program will be most beneficial. The question of medical care and medical needs of an aging population should receive careful study. The development of programs to retrain and rehabilitate middle-aged workers within various industries could best be carried out by an institute in association with industry. Comparisons of the cost of different programs of care for the aged are badly needed. Development of the programs for community service for retired people, as well as studies of living arrangements best adapted to old age, should be undertaken.

TEACHING FUNCTIONS

One of the greatest needs in gerontology—a need which has been largely overlooked—is that of education. Needed instruction ranges all the way from presentation of factual material to attract young students into research to the broad education of the general public in attitudes toward old age. Although the broad aspects of such an educational program could best be provided by an Institute of Gerontology, close association with a university would be desirable.

University instruction in gerontology.—There is a definite need for the organization of course material on our knowledge about aging for presentation to undergraduate and graduate students. At present, this material usually appears incidentally in a wide variety of courses, depending upon the interest and orientation of the particular instructor, whether it be in physiology, biochemistry, or psychology. More systematic instruction is imperative if we are to attract potential, competent research and professional workers into this field.

Just as the field of child development has evolved a body of knowledge about the physiology, biochemistry, and psychology of growth and development leading to improved methods of child care, so the field of gerontology must develop and offer training in the most appropriate methods of maintaining interests, developing new ones, reactivating old ones, retraining, and utilizing the capacities of the elderly people in the community for the good of the total society. Such instruction can best be offered in an institute where both research and service functions are operating. With the increasing number of elderly people in the population, it is obvious that universities will need to develop such training programs if they are to meet their full obligations to society.

Instruction in the field of geriatrics will of necessity develop within our medical schools and teaching hospitals. At the present time there are very few medical schools or hospitals which offer clinical training in geriatrics. An Institute of Gerontology associated with or operating a clinical center could well provide this essential medical training. Similarly, training in clinical psychology with respect to problems of counseling and adjustment in old people will be required. Only a few centers are now devoted to this type of work.

Training of social workers should also include course material on old age. Although there is an increasing awareness of the need for such training, few schools have yet organized and assembled the necessary materials for instruction.

Instruction for the aged.—The provision of instruction materials to broaden the horizons of elderly people and to prepare them for retirement is another important teaching function of an Institute of Gerontology. Association of the research institute with a university would make it possible to utilize members of the university staff for adult education programs. Furthermore, the classes could be made the basis for research on improved methods of instruction for adults. The offering of such course material within the framework of the institute would also draw older members of the community into other research programs of the institute.

Community education.—A program of educating communities with respect to the usefulness and potential capacities of elderly people is required. If we are to avoid economic difficulties in the future, we must begin now a program of education to combat the assumption that everyone becomes completely useless at a fixed chronological age of 60 or 65. We must develop programs to demonstrate to employers, labor unions, and the entire community that middle-aged and elderly people still have productive capacities and that it is essential for the good of the individual as well as for society in general to make full use of these capacities. Such a program is difficult and may require a long time for its completion, but the time to begin is now.

REHABILITATION AND CARE

Any organization dependent upon community cooperation must provide services that will meet community needs. The needs of elderly people may be outlined under three major headings, namely, the maintenance and expansion of interests and activities, medical care, and housing and living arrangements. The functions of this division are twofold—to provide essential services to old people and to serve as demonstration projects to devise and illustrate appropriate techniques for providing these services.

Maintenance and expansion of interests and activities.—All the courses for the aged mentioned in the previous section represent part of the program of broadening interests and maintaining activities in aging and elderly people. The program must be broadly conceived to include techniques for integrating and maintaining older people in community activities as well as offering opportunities for exercising their own creative abilities. This division must also develop programs which will investigate techniques most appropriate for the retraining of middle-aged workers. This program could cooperate with certain industries but should also look to the development of separate occupational units, including sheltered workshops. Occupational therapy programs best suited to the needs of elderly people should be evaluated. In connection with such programs, it will be important to provide outlets and uses for any articles produced. It would be the responsibility of this division to provide appropriate recreational and social programs for people in the community. The development of activities whereby the elderly can offer services to the community would fall into this department.

Medical care.—This department should be concerned not only with assessing the medical needs of the elderly people in the community but also with providing facilities for periodic physical examinations. In addition, an outpatient geriatric clinic should be operated.

With the full development of the institute, hospital care should be provided.

Housing and care.—This division should be responsible for the organization, operation, and construction of a variety of housing plans to be associated with the institute, and its program would include individual and group housing projects as well as sheltered-care programs and nursing homes. This division would look toward the ultimate development of an extensive community care program.

SUMMARY

Thus broadly conceived, the functions of an Institute of Gerontology should be research, teaching, and service to the aged. Ultimately, such an institute should coordinate and utilize the full capacities and potentialities of both a local and a university community.

A plan of organization for an institute to fulfill these functions is as follows:

An Institute of Gerontology should have physical form and substance and should provide for daily contacts among scientists from different disciplines. It should also provide common experimental rooms and space so that collaborative projects in different scientific disciplines can collect observations simultaneously on the same group of subjects.

The institute would have three major operating divisions: Research, Teaching, and Rehabilitation and Care, organized under the director, with two advisory committees appointed by the director and subject to his call. An organizational chart for the institute is suggested in Figure 10.

The director.—The success or failure of the program will depend upon the selection of an appropriate director. It will be necessary to find someone who is not only competent in a specific field of research but who also has a broad vision of the social and clinical problems of gerontology. He must have had research experience and must be able to command the respect of scientists. He must be able to work with clinicians, scientists, and lay people. He must be endowed with infectious enthusiasm. He will also need experience in organization and administration.

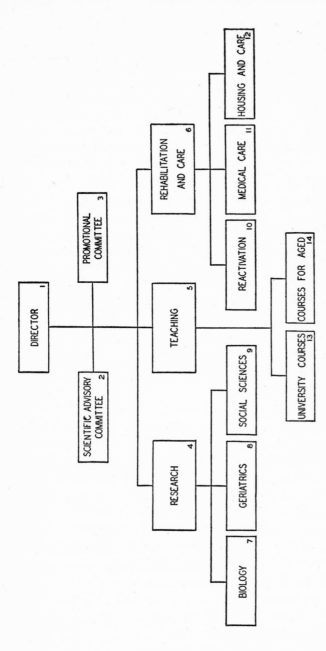

FIG. 10—Organization of an Institute of Gerontology.

Scientific advisory committee.—An advisory committee of scientists from different scientific disciplines should be appointed to advise the director and assist him in planning programs. Scientists from different universities and research centers should be included on this committee. In addition, at least two lay members interested in the problems of aging should be included. This advisory committee should have not more than 15 members or fewer than 10. The scientific members of this committee would not necessarily be active in the field of gerontology, but they should possess scientific stature in their chosen discipline. The membership of this committee should include a biologist, a physiologist, a biochemist, a psychologist, a clinician, a sociologist, a social work expert, and an economist, in addition to lay members.

Promotional committee.—The director should also have a committee of 6 to 12 persons who recognize the social importance of gerontology as well as the need for research. They should preferably be persons of influence within the local community and should be chosen to represent different social groups in our culture—for instance, business, labor, fraternal organizations, religious groups, Chambers of Commerce, and social work. This committee should include persons of local influence who can secure the active support of local organizations such as church groups, fraternal groups, labor unions, and businessmen's organizations. The function of this committee would be to secure local support for the institute in contributions of both time and money. The committee should also advise the director in planning community programs.

Research division.—The head of the research division should be a man with research training and accomplishment in the field of gerontology. Subject to the approval of the director, he would have responsibility for preparing budgets, directing research personnel, and planning the over-all research program. The three major fields of research would be biology, geriatrics, and social sciences. The biology unit would carry out studies on animals and would include the disciplines of biology, genetics, physiology, biochemistry, histology, anatomy, and biophysics. The second major unit, geriatrics, would include medical research on diseases peculiar to old age. The third unit, social sciences, would include the disciplines of psychology, sociology, economics, actuarial science, and statistics.

Teaching division.—This division should be in charge of someone with educational background and training. It would organize courses and curricula in two major categories. In the first category would be courses offered within the university leading to graduate training for research in the biological and social aspects of gerontology, in methods of care, the organization of programs for the rehabilitation and utilization of elderly people in the community, and individual counseling for the elderly. The other major category would include courses devised to prepare elderly people for retirement and community service. There should be courses in appreciation of music, art, literature, and science, and elementary instruction in such sciences as botany, horticulture, ornithology, and geology, as well as courses in the manual arts, such as bookbinding, metalwork, and weaving. These courses would be offered in the late afternoon and evening in order to attract members of the working community.

Rehabilitation and care division.—This division has a threefold purpose: (1) to provide services and satisfy needs of elderly people to attract them to the institute, (2) to provide a medium for practical application and demonstration of results from research projects, and (3) to provide expanded facilities for care and housing of elderly people. The person in charge of this division must have unlimited enthusiasm and a firm belief in the value of the project and must be a convincing promoter. The activities of this division include, first of all, the retraining and reactivation programs. The training courses would be supplied by the teaching division, but the development of sheltered workshops, occupational therapy programs, recreational and social activities, the organization of community service projects, and so on, must be the responsibilities of this unit. A second unit would consist of a hospital for chronic diseases. In connection with this hospital, clinics patterned after the fashion of the well-baby clinics in the field of child development should be organized. In addition, a regular outpatient geriatric clinic should be operated. The third unit of the division of rehabilitation and care would be concerned with housing of the elderly. In this connection, various types of housing units should be constructed, such as apartment buildings with certain community facilities—dining-room service, library, recreation, and housekeeping—for elderly couples. Small cottage units should also be established for rental to elderly couples for specific lengths of time, as, for example, three, six, or twelve months. Such a program could attract elderly people from many parts of the United States who would serve as experimental subjects for research programs in operation.

Briefly stated, this proposal is an over-all picture of what might be accomplished over a period of years in the field of gerontology. The proposed institute would serve the functions outlined and would represent a comprehensive program. Including as it does the building of domiciliary units, the hospital, the research building, recreational centers, and so on, the institute would require an extensive financial investment, and the cost of operation of such a program might well run to over a million dollars a year. This program offers a challenge well worth responding to.

THE DEVELOPMENT OF AN INSTITUTE OF GERONTOLOGY

With the ultimate goal of a comprehensive Institute of Gerontology outlined, we may turn to the progressive development of this program.

Stage 1.—The first step is to obtain a director with enthusiasm and vigor for the development of the institute. Since there is little point in attempting to initiate a strong research program until adequate groups of subjects are available for study, emphasis should first be placed on the development of the service divisions in order to attract middle-aged and elderly people into the program. Both the Scientific Advisory Committee and the Promotional Committee should be formed immediately, and meetings should be held to map out the broad aspects of the program. This program should be presented to as many local groups and organizations as possible through the activities of the Promotional Committee. All media of communication should be utilized to acquaint the community with the formation of the institute and its general service aims. The director should be appointed at professional rank with university tenure. The first programs developed in the center might well be devoted entirely to recreational and social activities, courses on preparation for retirement, and hobby craft. As more and more people are attracted to the center, the needs for university courses could be assessed. In all probability, such topics as current events, history, languages, art, music, and the manual arts will provide the nucleus from which additional courses could develop. Arrangements should be worked out with a local clinic whereby a health examination could be offered at perhaps a nominal fee.

Therefore, for Stage 1, the order of procedure would be as follows: (1) appointment of a director, (2) appointment of the Scientific Advisory Committee, (3) meeting of the Scientific Advisory Committee with the director to draw up the preliminary research programs, (4) appointment of the Promotional Committee, (5) indoctrination of the Promotional Committee with the aims and goals of the institute, (6) an active promotional campaign in the city to attract older people into the program, (7) setting up of physical quarters to house the program, and (8) appointment of additional staff members, including a physician and recreational director. Provision should be made for grants-in-aid to investigators working in the university and collaborating with the institute. Also, fellowships should be established in psychology, sociology, biology, physiology, biochemistry, zoology, genetics, and anatomy, which would be available to graduate students who are interested in carrying out research in the field of aging. The fellowship program is essential for the training of investigators needed to staff the research division of the institute at a later stage.

Stage 2.—As the program of the institute attracted a greater number and diversity of people, additional courses and activities could be added. Community projects with special committees devoted to improvement of schools, aid in hospitals, development of recreational facilities, Community Chest, and public health could be organized. These programs would create additional demands for courses for elderly people. Group projects on park care, gardening, and local history should be added. Expansion of the medical program to obtain repeat visits, with the addition of special diagnostic procedures carried out in collaboration with a local medical school or clinic, should follow. A full-time psychologist should be added to the staff, and a counseling center should be opened as an additional service. With ingenuity, many psychological test procedures could be disguised as recreational activities, and research in this area could be started. As soon as the counseling center began to receive a significant number of clients, the program of university courses could be initiated, using the institute for practice training. During this period, the grant-in-aid program as well as the research fellowship appropriations should be increased.

Stage 3.—As the service programs become established on a solid footing, research personnel in other disciplines should be appointed. These appointees might originally work within some department of the university, but at this time some plan should be made for providing laboratory facilities within the institute. At this stage, additional appointments of research personnel in the field of psychology and sociology might well be made. Although some chemical and physiological laboratories could easily be incorporated into the building used as a center, plans should be made for a building designed specifically for research. Such a building should be planned and designed so that, as the program developed, there would be land available for cottages, dormitories, and the hospital. During this period, research appointments should be made among biologists, physiologists, biochemists, and so on, to provide trained personnel for future development of the program. At the same time, retraining programs should be worked out in collaboration with industry.

Stage 4.—By this time, the service program should be in full operation so that university courses could begin to use the center for teaching and demonstration purposes. Constant growth of the staff of the service departments should continue, so that chiefs in the various service units would need to be designated.

Stage 5.—At this stage, the needs of both the teaching and service programs would call for the establishment of some types of sheltered workshops. The operating programs and the service departments should provide facilities whereby a program of short courses for the training of professional workers in the field could be set up. These courses could be offered at a summer session or at other appropriate times and would include demonstrations at the center for effective methods of organizing activities for elderly people. It would be expected that workers would come to the university for these courses from all parts of the state and the nation. At the same time, summer courses for middle-aged and elderly people could be set up for the express purpose of widening their horizons and preparing them for retirement and community service.

Stage 6.—The next step in the development of the program would be to secure adequate land for building a research center with dormitories, apartments, and small cottages for living programs for the aged. Members of the institute serving in other parts of the university should then be transferred to the central building for their research activities. Further coordinated interdisciplinary projects could be planned and put into operation.

Stage 7.—By this time, a research hospital for the study of chronic diseases with programs in geriatric and medical care as well as the clinical training in geriatrics and geriatric nursing should be provided. As part of the medical program, a number of nursing homes should be built and maintained in association with the hospital. Thus it is possible to develop the entire institute program in step-wise fashion.

REFERENCES

Chapter 2

1. Committee on Aging, Federal Security Agency. *Fact Book on Aging.* Washington, D.C., Government Printing Office, 1952, 62 pp.
2. Bureau of the Census. *1950 Census of the Population, Advance Reports,* Series PC-9, No. 1; and *Current Population Reports, Population Estimates,* Series P-25, No. 37.
3. Smith, T. L. "Migration of the Aged," in New York State Joint Legislative Committee on Problems of the Aging, *Growing with the Years.* Legislative Doc. No. 32, 1954, pp. 69–80.
4. Hitt, H. L. "The Role of Migration in Population Changes Among the Aged," *Am. Sociol. Rev.,* 19 : 194–200, 1954.
5. Hamilton, J. B. "The Role of Testicular Secretions as Indicated by the Effects of Castration in Man and by Studies of Pathological Conditions and the Short Lifespan Associated with Maleness," *Recent Prog. Hormone Res.,* 3 : 257–324, 1948.
6. Committee on Aging, Federal Security Agency. *Op. cit.*
7. Bureau of the Census. *Current Population Reports, Population Characteristics,* Series P-20, No. 10.
8. Dublin, L. I., A. J. Lotka, and M. Spiegelman. *Length of Life.* Rev. ed. New York, Ronald Press, 1949, pp. 50, 96.

Chapter 3

1. New York State Joint Legislative Committee on Problems of the Aging, Legislative Documents. *Birthdays Don't Count,* No. 61 (1948), 326 pp.; *Never Too Old,* No. 32 (1949), 216 pp.; *Young at Any Age,* No. 12 (1950), 192 pp.; *No Time to Grow Old,* No. 12 (1951), 316 pp.; *Age Is No Barrier,* No. 35 (1952), 171 pp.; *Enriching the Years,* No. 32 (1953), 199 pp.; *Growing with the Years,* No. 32 (1954), 159 pp.; *Making the Years Count,* No. 32 (1955), 162 pp.; *New Channels for the Golden Years,* No. 33 (1956), 151 pp.
   Proceedings of the Second Conference on Problems of Making a Living While Growing Old. Philadelphia, Temple University, Bureau of Economic and Business Research, 1953, 414 pp.

Tuckman, J., and I. Lorge. *Retirement and the Industrial Worker; Prospect and Reality*. New York, Columbia University, Bureau of Publications, 1953, 105 pp.

2. New York State Joint Legislative Committee on Problems of the Aging. *Op. cit.*

3. Donahue, W. *Earning Opportunities for Older Workers.* Ann Arbor, University of Michigan Press, 1955, 277 pp.

Odell, C. E. "Employment Services for Older Workers," *Ann. Am. Acad. Pol. & Soc. Sci.*, **279** : 171–79, 1952.

U.S. Department of Labor, Bureau of Employment Security. "Services for Older Workers; the Need for Developing Work Opportunities," *Employ. Sec. Rev.*, **21** : 8, 1954.

Breckinridge, E. L. *Effective Use of Older Workers.* New York, Wilcox and Follett, 1953, 224 pp.

4. Derber, M. (ed.) *The Aged and Society.* Champaign, Ill., Industrial Relations Research Association, 1950, 237 pp.

McConnell, J. W. "The Utilization of Older Workers; Preserving Social and Economic Values," *Personnel,* **29** : 314–21, 1953.

5. Mathiasen, G. (ed.) *Criteria for Retirement.* New York, Putnam, 1953, 233 pp.

6. Friedmann, E. A., and R. J. Havighurst. *The Meaning of Work and Retirement.* Chicago, University of Chicago Press, 1954, 197 pp.

7. Havighurst, R. J., and R. Albrecht. *Older People.* New York, Longmans, Green, 1953, 415 pp.

8. U.S. Department of Labor, Bureau of Labor Statistics. *Employment and Economic Status of Older Men and Women.* Washington, D.C., Government Printing Office, Bull. No. 1092, May 1952, 57 pp.

9. Clark, L. G. F., and A. C. Dunn. *Aging in Industry.* New York, Philosophical Library, 1956, 146 pp.

10. U.S. Department of Labor, Bureau of Employment Security. *Older Worker Adjustment to Labor Market Practices. An Analysis of Experience in Seven Major Labor Markets.* Washington, D.C., Government Printing Office, Bull. No. R151, September 1956, 269 pp.

11. Dorfman, R. "The Labor Force Status of Persons Aged 65 and Over," *Am. Econ. Rev.*, **54** : 644, 1954.

Steiner, P. O., and R. Dorfman. *Economic Status of the Aged.* Berkeley, University of California Press, 1957, 320 pp.

12. New York State Joint Legislative Committee on Problems of the Aging. *Op. cit.*

13. New York State Joint Legislative Committee on Problems of the Aging. *Op. cit.*

14. California Department of Industrial Relations. *Middle Aged and Older Workers.* Special Bull. Nos. 1 and 2, 1930, 35 pp.

15. Peterson, R. L. "Older Workers and Their Job Effectiveness," *Geriatrics,* 10: 34–38, 1955.
16. Tuckman, J., and I. Lorge. "Expert's Biases About Older Workers," *Science,* 115: 685–87, 1952.
17. Williamson, L. C. "Senior Workers Please Employers," *Employ. Sec. Rev.,* 22: 3–5, 1955.
    Smith, M. W. "Older Workers' Efficiency in Jobs of Various Types," *Personnel J.,* 32: 19–23, 1953.
18. Kossoris, M. D. "Absenteeism and Injury Experiences of Older Workers," *Mon. Labor Rev.,* 67: 16–19, 1948.
19. Sayer, H. D. "Compensation Act Is No Bar to Elderly; Rates Do Not Reflect Age of Worker," *Eastern Underwriter,* 48: 81, 1948.
20. Breckinridge, E. L. *Op. cit.*
    Donahue, W. *Op. cit.*
    New York State Joint Legislative Committee on Problems of the Aging. *Op. cit.*
21. New York State Joint Legislative Committee on Problems of the Aging. *Op. cit.*
22. Shock, N. W. "Physiological Aspects of Mental Disorders in Later Life," Chap. IV in Oscar J. Kaplan (ed.), *Mental Disorders in Later Life.* 2d ed. Stanford, Calif., Stanford University Press, 1956, pp. 47–97.
    Shock, N. W. "Some Physiological Aspects of Aging in Man," *Bull. N.Y. Acad. Med.,* 32: 268–83, 1956.
    Shock, N. W. "Age Changes in Some Physiologic Processes," *Geriatrics,* 12: 40–48, 1957.
23. Shock, N. W. "Skill and Employment," *Pub. Health Rep.,* 70: 851–54, 1955.
    Shock, N. W. "Skill and Employment," in J. E. Anderson (ed.), *Psychological Aspects of Aging.* Washington, D.C., Am. Psychol. Assoc., Inc., 1956, pp. 249–53.
    Welford, A. T. *Skill and Age.* London, The Nuffield Foundation, Oxford University Press, 1951, 161 pp.
24. Clay, H. M. "A Study of Performance in Relation to Age at Two Printing Works," *J. Geront.,* 11: 417–24, 1956.
25. Mathiasen, G. (ed.). *Flexible Retirement: Evolving Policies and Programs for Industry and Labor.* New York, Putnam, 1957, 226 pp.
26. Barkin, S. "Jobs for Older Workers," *J. Geront.,* 7: 426–30, 1952.
27. Donahue, W. *Op. cit.*
28. Pressey, S. L. "The Older Psychologist; His Potentials and His Problems," *Am. Psychol.,* 10: 163–65, 1955.
29. Dr. D. Bruce Dill, U.S. Army Chemical Warfare Laboratories, Army Chemical Center, Maryland, is chairman of the committee.

30. Stern, J. "Possible Effects of Automation on Older Workers," *Voc. Guid. Quart.*, 4: 41–45, 1955–56.

Chapter 4

1. Roney, J. L. "Twenty Years of Public Assistance," *Soc. Sec. Bull.*, 18: 17–23, August 1955.
2. Bureau of the Census. *Current Population Reports, Consumer Income*. Series P-60, No. 14, Dec. 31, 1953.
   Steiner, P. O., and R. Dorfman. *Economic Status of the Aged*. Berkeley, University of California Press, 1957, 320 pp.
   Miller, H. P. *Income of the American People*. New York, Wiley, 1955, 206 pp.
3. Committee on Aging, Federal Security Agency. *Fact Book on Aging*. Washington, D.C., Government Printing Office, 1952, 62 pp.
4. Corson, J. J., and J. W. McConnell. *Economic Needs of Older People*. New York, Twentieth Century Fund, 1956, 533 pp.
5. *A Study of Industrial Retirement Plans*. New York, Bankers Trust Company, 1956, 177 pp.
6. United Mine Workers of America. *Chronology of the United Mine Workers of America Welfare and Retirement Fund*. Washington, D.C., 1949, 15 pp.
7. Cohen, W. J., R. M. Ball, and R. J. Myers. "Social Security Act Amendments, 1954; a Summary and Legislative History," *Soc. Sec. Bull.*, 17: 3–18, September 1954.
8. Schottland, C. I. "Social Security Amendments of 1956; a Summary and Legislative History," *Soc. Sec. Bull.*, 19: 3–15, September 1956.
9. Johnson, G. E. "A Safe Retirement Income? TIAA Plan Reflects Changes in Living Costs and Purchasing Power," *Trusts & Estates Magazine*, Fiduciary Publishers, 1955.

Chapter 5

1. Commission on Chronic Illness. *Chronic Illness in the United States*. Vol. II. *Care of the Long-Term Patient*. Cambridge, Harvard University Press, 1956, 606 pp.
2. National Health Survey, 1935–36. *Sickness and Medical Care Series*. Bull. No. 6, National Institutes of Health. Washington, D.C., Government Printing Office, 1939.
3. *The States and Their Older Citizens*. Chicago, Council of State Governments, 1955, 176 pp. (Table 41).
4. Sheldon, J. H. *Social Medicine of Old Age. Report of an Inquiry in Wolverhampton*. London, Oxford University Press, 1948, 239 pp.
   Magnuson, P. B. (chairman), The President's Commission on the Health Needs of the Nation. *Building America's Health*: I. *Findings and Recommendations,* 80 pp.; II. *America's Health Status; Needs*

and Resources, 320 pp.; III. America's Health Status; Needs and Resources, A Statistical Appendix, 299 pp. Washington, D.C., Government Printing Office, 1953.

Ciocco, A., and P. S. Lawrence. Illness Among Older People in Hagerstown, Maryland. Federal Security Agency, Public Health Service, Pub. No. 170. Washington, D.C., Government Printing Office, 1952, pp. 26–37.

Jackson, E. H. "Morbidity Among Males and Females at Specific Ages —Eastern Health District of Baltimore," Milbank Mem. Fd. Quart. Bull., 28: 429–48, 1950.

Pemberton, J. "The Measurement of Health in Groups of Elderly People Living at Home," in Old Age in the Modern World. London, E. & S. Livingston, 1955, pp. 364–74.

Simonds, W. H., and A. Stewart. "Old People Living in Dorset; a Sociomedical Survey of Private Households," Brit. J. Prev. Soc. Med., 8: 139–46, 1954.

Ström, A. "An Investigation of the Living Conditions and Health of Persons Aged 70 Years or More in Norway," J. Geront., 11: 178–84, 1956.

5. Kutner, B., D. Fanshel, A. M. Togo, and T. S. Langner. Five Hundred Over Sixty. A Community Survey on Aging. New York, Russell Sage Foundation, 1956, 345 pp.

6. Havighurst, R. J., and R. Albrecht. Older People. New York, Longmans, Green, 1953, 415 pp.

7. Jones, H. B. "A Special Consideration of the Aging Process, Disease and Life Expectancy," Adv. Biol. Med. Physics, 4: 281–337, 1956.

8. Kutner, B., D. Fanshel, A. M. Togo, and T. S. Langner. Op. cit.

9. Stieglitz, E. J. (ed.). Geriatric Medicine. Medical Care of Later Maturity. 3d ed. Philadelphia, Lippincott, 1954, 718 pp.

10. Seegal, D. "Some Comments on the Medical Management of the Older Person," Res. Publ. Ass. nerv. ment. Dis., 35: 245–48, 1956.

11. Stieglitz, E. J. "Difficulties in Geriatric Diagnosis," Md. St. Med. J., 4: 517–26, 1955.

12. Monroe, R. T. "Medical Problems of Old Age," New England J. Med., 240: 57–60, 1949.

Monroe, R. T. Diseases in Old Age; A Clinical and Pathological Study of 7,941 Individuals Over 61 Years of Age. Cambridge, Harvard University Press, 1951, 407 pp.

13. Gitman, L. "Blueprint for a Geriatric Center," Geriatrics, 10: 487–90, 1955.

14. Kutner, B., D. Fanshel, A. M. Togo, and T. S. Langner. Op. cit.

15. Brewster, A. W., and D. McCamman. Health Costs of the Aged. Washington, D.C., Government Printing Office, May 1956, 126 pp.

16. Standish, S., Jr., B. Bennett, and B. C. Houghton. *Why Patients See Doctors.* Seattle, University of Washington Press, 1955, p. 5.
17. Dickinson, F. G. *Age and Sex Distribution of Hospital Patients.* American Medical Association, Bureau of Medical Economic Research, Bull. No. 97, 1955.
18. Brewster, A. W., and D. McCamman. *Op. cit.,* p. 53.
19. Solon, J., D. W. Roberts, D. E. Krueger, and A. M. Baney. "Nursing Homes, Their Patients and Their Care. A Study of Nursing Homes and Similar Long-Term Care Facilities in 13 States," *Pub. Health Monog.,* No. 46, PHS Pub. No. 503. Washington, D.C., Government Printing Office, 1957, 55 pp.
20. *Standards of Care for Older People in Institutions. Section 1. Suggested Standards for Homes for the Aged and Nursing Homes.* New York, National Social Welfare Assembly, Committee on the Aging, 1953, 112 pp.
21. Bluestone, E. M. "The Principles and Practice of Home Care," *J.A.M.A.,* **155**: 1379–82, 1954.
22. Warren, M. W. "The Home Nursing of the Aged Sick," *Practitioner,* **174**: 567–73, 1955.
23. Rusk, H. A. "Geriatrics and Rehabilitation," *Geriatrics,* **6**: 143–50, 1951.
    Rusk, H. A., and E. J. Taylor. "Rehabilitation," *Ann. Am. Acad. Pol. & Soc. Sci.,* **273**: 138–43, 1951.
24. Zeman, F. D. "The Medical Organization of the Modern Home for the Aged," *J. Geront.,* **5**: 262–65, 1950.
25. Zeman, F. D. *Still Going Places! Active Management of Disability in the Aged.* Film. Brooklyn, N.Y., Pfizer Laboratories.
26. Warren, M. W. "The Medical Care and Rehabilitation of Elderly People," *Adv. Sci., London,* **6**: 18, 1949.
    Warren, M. W. "Retraining the Elderly Hemiplegic," *Geriatrics,* **8**: 198–203, 1953.
27. Howell, T. H. *Old Age: Some Practical Points in Geriatrics and Gerontology.* 2d ed. London, H. K. Lewis, 1950, 108 pp.
    Howell, T. H. "The Half-Way House for the Aged Sick; an Experiment in Social Medicine," *Mon. Bull. Min. Health, Publ. Health Lab. Serv., London,* **10**: 186–88, 1951.
28. Sheldon, J. H. "Problems of Geriatric Care," *J. Am. Geriat. Soc.,* **4**: 642–47, 1956.
29. Amulree, Lord B. W. S. *Adding Life to Years.* Nat. Council Soc. Serv., Inc. London, Bannisdale Press, 1951, 101 pp.
30. Cosin, L. Z. "A Statistical Analysis of Geriatric Rehabilitation," *J. Geront.,* **7**: 570–78, 1952.

31. McCamman, D., and A. W. Brewster. "Voluntary Health Insurance Coverage of Aged Beneficiaries of Old Age and Survivors Insurance," *Soc. Sec. Bull.,* 17 : 3–11, August 1954.
32. Wilson, F. J. "Your Group Hospitalization Policy," *Retirement Life,* 32 : 2, 1957.
33. Pennsylvania State Medical Society, Commission on Geriatrics. "Age and Costs of Medical Care. Supplement Report," *Penn. Med. J.,* 58 : 104–7, 1955.
34. Tibbitts, C. "Aging; Implications for Public Health," *Pub. Health Rep., Wash.,* 67 : 121–26, 1952.
35. Scheele, L. A. "Better Care for Older People," *Pub. Health Rep., Wash.,* 69 : 455–60, 1954.
36. Burney, L. E. "Programs for the Aged," *Pub. Health Rep., Wash.,* 71 : 1168–69, 1956.

Chapter 6

1. Donahue, W. (ed.). *Housing the Aging.* Ann Arbor, University of Michigan Press, 1954, 280 pp.
2. Fisher, J. "Trends in Institutional Care of the Aged," *Soc. Sec. Bull.,* 16 : 9–13, October 1953.
3. Anderson, E. M. "Existing and Preferred Housing of Aged Couples of Moderate Income in Manhattan, Kansas." Master's thesis. Kansas State Teachers College of Agriculture and Applied Science, 1951.
4. Webber, I. L. *The Retired Population of St. Petersburg; Its Characteristics and Social Situation.* Tallahassee, Florida State Improvement Commission, 1950, 150 pp.
5. Hunter, W., and H. Maurice. *Older People Tell Their Story.* Ann Arbor, University of Michigan Press, 1953, 97 pp.
6. *Old Age in Rhode Island.* Providence, Governor's Commission to Study Problems of the Aged, 1953, 143 pp.
7. *Housing an Aging Population.* New York, American Public Health Association, Committee on the Hygiene of Housing, 1953, 92 pp.
8. Johnson, R. J., and M. A. Pond. "Health Standards of Housing for the Aging Population," *J. Geront.,* 7 : 254–58, 1952.
9. *Standards of Design; Housing for the Elderly.* Boston, Massachusetts State Housing Board, 1954, 17 pp.
10. *Housing Manual, 1949.* Great Britain, Ministry of Health. London, H. M. Stationery Office, 1949, 150 pp. Supplement, 1951, 44 pp.
11. Alt, E. *Standards of Care for Older People in Institutions. Section I. Suggested Standards for Homes for the Aged and Nursing Homes.* New York, National Social Welfare Assembly, Committee on the Aging, 1953, 112 pp.

12. Announced in *Architectural Record,* May 1956.
13. Belluchi, P. "Prize Winning Designs and Report of the Jury; Home for Aged Competition," *Archit. Rec.,* **122**: 161–68, 1957.
14. Silk, L. S. "The Housing Circumstances of the Aged in the United States, 1950," *J. Geront.,* **7**: 87–91, 1952.
15. Hoyt, G. C. "The Life of the Retired in a Trailer Park," *Am. J. Sociol.,* **59**: 361–70, 1954.
16. Meister, K. P., "The Methodist Church Program for Care of Aged and Chronically Ill." *Chron. Ill. Newsletter,* **3**: 2–3, 1952.
17. Swaim, W. T., Jr. "Advantages of Decentralization," *Presbyterian Home News,* **21** (1): 19–23, 1957.
18. Kleemeier, R. W. "Moosehaven; Congregate Living in a Community of the Retired," *Am. J. Sociol.,* **59**: 347–51, 1954.
19. Kleemeier, R. W. "The Effect of a Work Program on Adjustment Attitudes in an Aged Population," *J. Geront.,* **6**: 372–79, 1951.
20. Kleemeier, R. W. "The Research Program at Moosehaven, Florida," in H. E. Jones, *Research on Aging.* New York, Social Science Research Council, 1950, pp. 10–14.
21. Bureau of the Census. *U.S. Census of Population, 1950. Institutional Population.* Special Reports, Part 2, Chap. C, pp. 16–18.
22. United States Senate, Committee on Labor and Public Welfare. *Studies of the Aged and Aging.* Vol. 6. *Care of the Aging by the Veterans Administration.* Washington, D.C., Government Printing Office, 1956, 92 pp.
23. Casalena, K. F. "A Foster Home Program for the Aged," *Catholic Charities Rev.,* **65**: 60–63, 1951.
24. Cryan, E. "Foster Home Care for Older People," *Am. J. Nursing,* **54**: 954–56, 1954.
25. Posner, W. *A Foster Home Program for Older Persons.* New York, National Social Welfare Assembly, Committee on Aging, November 1952, 24 pp.
    Fox, F. "Home Care Programs of Homes for the Aged," *Jewish Soc. Serv. Quart.,* **29**: 302–9, 1953.

Chapter 7

1. Donahue, W. *Education for Later Maturity.* New York, Whiteside, 1955, 338 pp.
2. Carlson, A. J. "Can Continuous Adult Education Add More Life to the Later Years?" in *Old Age in the Modern World.* London, E. & S. Livingstone, 1955, pp. 610–11.
3. Gilbert, J. G. *Understanding Old Age.* New York, Ronald Press, 1952, 422 pp.
4. Lorge, I. "Gerontology (Later Maturity)," in P. R. Farnsworth and

Q. McNemar (eds.), *Ann. Rev. Psych.,* 1956, pp. 349–64.

Shock, N. W. "Gerontology (Later Maturity)," in C. P. Stone and D. W. Taylor (eds.), *Ann. Rev. Psych.,* 1951, pp. 353–70.

5. Hand, S. E. *A Review of Physiological and Psychological Changes in Aging and Their Implications for Teachers of Adults.* Florida State Department of Education, June 1956.

6. Lorge, I., and R. Kushner. "Characteristics of Adults Basic to Education," *Rev. Educ. Res.,* **20**: 174–84, 1950.

7. Tibbitts, C. "Aging and Living. A Report of the First Course Offered to Assist People in Making Adjustments to Old Age," *Adult Educ. Bull.,* **13**: 204–11, 1948.

8. Peterson, R. L. "A University Extension Course in Gerontology," *J. Geront.,* **6**: 39–42, 1951.

9. Harris, D. B. "Maturity and Aging; a Course in the Institute of Child Welfare of the University of Minnesota," *J. Geront.,* **3**: 18–20, 1948.

10. Reals, W. H. "Education of the Aging in Institutions of Higher Learning," *Sch. & Soc.,* **79**: 177–84, 1954.

11. Little, M. H., and E. Shanas. "A Preventive Mental Hygiene Course for Older Adults," *Adult Educ.,* **3**: 84–87, 1953.

12. Shanas, E., and J. Bower. "Correspondence Courses," in W. Donahue (ed.), *Education for Later Maturity.* New York, Whiteside, 1955, pp. 138–45.

13. Blackshear, O. T. "The Public Library Serves the Aging," *Wisconsin Library Bull.,* **52**: 60–65, 1956.

14. Fund for Adult Education, 320 Westchester Avenue, White Plains, New York.

15. Andrus, R. "The Cold Spring Project; the Value of a Small Residential Group in the Study of Change and Growth in College Graduates Over 60," in *Old Age in the Modern World.* London, E. & S. Livingstone, 1955, p. 616.

16. Proceedings of these conferences have been published by the University of Michigan Press under the following titles:

Tibbitts, C. (ed.). *Living Through the Older Years.* 1950, 248 pp.

Donahue, W., and C. Tibbitts (eds.). *Planning the Older Years.* 1950, 248 pp.

Donahue, W., and C. Tibbitts (eds.). *Growing in the Older Years.* 1951, 204 pp.

Donahue, W., J. Rae, Jr., and R. B. Berry (eds.). *Rehabilitation of the Older Worker.* 1953, 200 pp.

Donahue, W. (ed.). *Housing the Aging.* 1954, 280 pp.

Donahue, W. (ed.). *Earning Opportunities for the Older Worker.* 1955, 277 pp.

17. For annual volumes published by the New York State Legislative Committee on Problems of the Aging, see first item under Reference 1, Chapter 3.

18. The proceedings of these conferences have been published by the University of Florida Press under the following titles:

Smith, T. L. (ed.). *Problems of America's Aging Population.* 1951, 117 pp.

Smith, T. L. (ed.). *Living in the Later Years.* 1952, 176 pp.

Machlachlan, J. M. (ed.). *Health in the Later Years.* 1953, 125 pp.

Hurff, G. B. (ed.). *Economic Problems of Retirement.* 1954, 180 pp.

Webber, I. L. (ed.). *Aging and Retirement.* 1955, 142 pp.

Webber, I. L. (ed.). *Aging: A Current Appraisal.* 1956, 179 pp.

19. Gilbert, J. G. *Op. cit.*

Smith, E. S. *The Dynamics of Aging.* New York, Norton, 1956, 191 pp.

De Gruchy, C. *Creative Old Age.* San Francisco, Geertz Printing Co., 1946, 143 pp.

20. Boas, E. P. *Add Life to Your Years.* New York, McBride, 1954, 278 pp.

Johnson, W. *The Years After 50.* New York, McGraw-Hill, 1947, 153 pp.

Howell, T. H. *Our Advancing Years.* London, Phoenix House, 1953, 192 pp.

Stieglitz, E. J. *The Second Forty Years.* Philadelphia, Lippincott, 1946, 317 pp.

Lerrigo, C. H. *The Better Half of Your Life.* New York, John Day, 1951, 270 pp.

Munro, D. C. *You Can Live Longer Than You Think.* New York, Bartholomew House, 1948, 211 pp.

U.S. Federal Security Agency. *Education for a Long and Useful Life.* Office of Education, 1950, Bull. No. 6, 32 pp.

21. Arthur, J. K. *How to Help Older People.* Philadelphia, Lippincott, 1954, 500 pp.

Stern, E. M. *You and Your Aging Parents.* New York, A. A. Wyn, 1952, 212 pp.

22. Kaplan, J. *A Social Program for Older People.* Minneapolis, University of Minnesota Press, 1953, 158 pp.

Woods, J. H. *Helping Older People Enjoy Life.* New York, Harper, 1953, 139 pp.

23. Gumpert, M. *You Are Younger Than You Think.* Cleveland and New York, World Publishing Co., 1947, 244 pp.

Lawton, G. *Aging Successfully.* New York, Columbia University Press, 1946, 266 pp.

Lawton, G. *New Goals for Old Age.* New York, Columbia University Press, 1943, 210 pp.

Pitkin, W. B. *Life Begins at Forty.* New York, McGraw-Hill, 1932, 175 pp.

Giles, R. *How to Retire—And Enjoy It.* New York, Whittlesey House, McGraw-Hill, 1949, 268 pp.

Jeffreys, R. J. *Life Will Begin at 100.* Columbus, Ohio, Capitol College Press, 1955, 239 pp.

Lieb, C. W. *Outwitting Your Years.* New York, Prentice-Hall, 1949, 278 pp.

Crampton, C. W. *Live Long and Like It.* New York, Public Affairs Committee, 1948, Pamphlet No. 139, 32 pp.

24. *Successful Retirement Annual,* 22 East Twelfth Street, Cincinnati 10, Ohio.

25. *Journal of Lifetime Living,* 55 West 42d Street, New York 36, New York.

26. *Senior Citizen,* 1129 Vermont Avenue, Northwest, Washington 5, D.C.

27. National Association of Retired Civil Service Employees, 1625 Connecticut Avenue, Washington 9, D.C.

28. *Mature Years,* Methodist Episcopal Church, The Graded Press, 810 Broadway, Nashville, Tennessee.

29. Gerontological Society, Inc., 660 South Kingshighway Boulevard, St. Louis 10, Missouri.

30. *Aging.* Washington 25, D.C., Government Printing Office.

31. Mrs. Geneva Mathiasen, Secretary, National Social Welfare Assembly, 345 East 46th Street, New York 17, New York.

32. Film Library, Pfizer Laboratories, 630 Flushing Avenue, Brooklyn 6, New York.

33. Retirement Council, Inc., 342 Madison Avenue, New York 17, New York.

34. Mathiasen, G. (ed.). *Flexible Retirement.* New York, Putnam, 1957, 226 pp.

35. Federal Security Agency. *Man and His Years.* Raleigh, N.C., Health Publications Institute, Inc., 1951, 311 pp.

36. An outline of the content of this course may be found in the *Bulletin of the Institute of Gerontology* (State University of Iowa), 4: 1–2, 1957.

37. Zeman, F. D. "Teaching Geriatrics: Basic Principles and Syllabus of Course Now in the Fifth Year," *J. Geront.,* 4: 48–52, 1949.

38. The lectures given in this series have been published in the *Bulletin of the New York Academy of Medicine,* 1956.

39. Papers presented have been published in the January and February 1957 issue of *Geriatrics.*

40. I am indebted to Miss Ollie A. Randall for a large part of the information in this section.

41. Hamrin, G. "A Training Program for Directors of Homes for the Aged," *Geriatrics,* 10: 391–93, 1955.

42. J. E. Kirk, Editor, 5600 Arsenal Street, St. Louis 10, Missouri.

43. Dr. Thomas H. McGavack, President, New York Medical College, 5th Avenue and 105th Street, New York 29, New York.

44. American Psychological Association, 1333 Sixteenth Street, N.W., Washington 6, D.C.

45. Dr. S. L. Pressey, Ohio State University, is chairman of the committee.

46. Abstracts of papers presented have been published in *Revue Médicale de Liége,* 5: 593–732, 1950.

47. Abstracts of papers were published in the *Journal of Gerontology,* 6: (Suppl. to No. 3), 1–201, 1951. A summary of the Congress may be found in the *Journal of Gerontology,* 7: 259–90, 1952.

48. These papers have been published in *Old Age in the Modern World.* Edinburgh and London, E. & S. Livingstone, Ltd., 1955, 647 pp.

49. Verzár, F. (ed.). *Experimentelle Alternsforschung.* Basel and Stuttgart, Birkhäuser Verlag, 1956, Suppl. IV, 290 pp.

50. *Libro de resumenes.* Mexico, Primer Congreso Pan Americano de Gerontologia, September 1956, 332 pp.

51. *Journal of Gerontology,* published by the Gerontological Society, Inc., 660 South Kingshighway Boulevard, St. Louis 10, Missouri.
    Geriatrics, published by Lancet Publications, Inc., 84 South Tenth Street, Minneapolis, Minnesota, under the editorship of Dr. W. C. Alvarez.

52. *Acta Gerontologica Japonica, Acta Gerontologica* (Milano), *Archives of Gerontology* (Japan), *De Senectute* (Switzerland), *Geriatria* (Buenos Aires), *Geriatrics* (U.S.A.), *Geron* (Finland), *Gerontologia* (Switzerland), *Giornale di Gerontologia* (Italy), *Journal of the American Geriatrics Society* (U.S.A.), *Journal of Chronic Diseases* (U.S.A.), *Journal of Gerontology* (U.S.A.), *Longevità* (Italy), *Revista de Geriatria* (Torreon, Mex.), *Rivista di Gerontologia e Geriatria* (Italy), and *Zeitschrift für Altersforschung* (Germany).

53. Proceedings of the tenth (1948) through the final (fifteenth—1953) conferences have been published by the Josiah Macy, Jr. Foundation, N. W. Shock, Editor.

54. Published in *Federation Proceedings,* 15: 938–64, 1956.

55. Moore, J. E., H. H. Merritt, and R. J. Masselink (eds.). *The Neurologic and Psychiatric Aspects of the Disorders of Ageing.* Vol. 35 of *Res. Publ. Ass. nerv. ment. Dis.,* 1956, 307 pp.

56. Ciba Foundation. *Colloquia on Ageing.* Vol. I. *General Aspects.* London, J. A. Churchill, 1955, 255 pp.
57. Ciba Foundation. *Colloquia on Ageing.* Vol. II. *Ageing in Transient Tissues.* London, J. A. Churchill, 1956, 263 pp.
58. Ciba Foundation. *Colloquia on Ageing.* Vol. III. *Methodology of the Study of Ageing.* Edited by G. E. W. Wolstenholme and C. M. O'Connor. London, J. A. Churchill, 1957, 202 pp.

Chapter 8

1. Federal Security Agency. *Man and His Years.* Raleigh, N.C., Health Publications Institute, Inc., 1951, 311 pp.
2. U.S. Senate, Committee on Labor and Public Welfare. *Studies of the Aged.* Vol. I. *Federal and State Activities.* Washington, D.C., Government Printing Office, 1956, 309 pp.
3. The states that have established commissions, or committees, are as follows: California (1952), Colorado (1955), Connecticut (1945), Florida (1950–53), Illinois (1950), Indiana (1955), Kansas (1953–54), Maine (1953), Massachusetts (1954), Michigan (1951–52, 1955), Minnesota (1951), New Hampshire (1953–54), New Jersey (1954), New Mexico (1952), New York (1947), North Carolina (1955), Ohio (1953–55), Oregon (1953–54), Pennsylvania (1951–53), Rhode Island (1953), Vermont (1953–54), Washington, (1952), West Virginia (1951–52), and Wisconsin (1951).
   The States and Their Older Citizens. Chicago, Council of State Governments, 1955, 176 pp.
4. Examples of published reports are:
   Report of the Commission. Hartford, Connecticut, Commission on the Potentials of Aging, 1954, 125 pp.
   Golden Years. Augusta, Maine, Committee on Aging, 1954, 36 pp.
   Minnesota's Aging Citizens Commission on Aging. St. Paul, Minnesota, Commission on Aging, 1955, 2d Report, 43 pp.
   Report of the Governor's Committee to Study Problems of the Aging. Salem, Oregon, Governor's Committee, 1954, 41 pp.
   Governor's Commission to Study Problems of the Aged. Providence, Rhode Island, Governor's Commission, 1953, 143 pp.
5. *Proceedings of the Governor's Conference on the Problems of the Aging.* Sacramento, California, Governor's Conference, 1951, 296 pp.
6. *Charter for the Aging.* Albany, New York, Governor's Conference, 1955, 659 pp.
7. *Background Material for Governor's Conference on Aging.* Olympia, Washington, Governor's Conference, 1955, 70 pp.
8. U.S. Senate. Committee on Labor and Public Welfare. *Op. cit.,* pp. 191–274.

9. In May 1956, the Railroad Retirement Board's request for representation on the council was granted.

10. U.S. Senate. Committee on Labor and Public Welfare. *Op. cit.,* pp. 53–110.
Also summarized in *Soc. Sec. Bull.,* **19**: 3–7, 1956.

11. Fuchs, I., and H. Levine. "The Hodson Community Center," *J. Geront.,* 1 : 55–59, 1946.

12. Bowen, G. E. "Philadelphia's Recreational Project for Older People," *J. Geront.,* 3 : 215–19, 1948.
See also:
Meyer, H. D. *A Manual of Organization Clubs for Senior Citizens.* North Carolina Recreation Commission, April 1956, No. 19, 31 pp.
Kaplan, J. *A Social Program for Older People.* Minneapolis, University of Minnesota Press, 1953, 158 pp.
Kubie, S. H., and G. Landau. *Group Work With the Aged.* New York, International Universities Press, 1953, 214 pp.
Woods, J. H. *Helping Older People Enjoy Life.* New York, Harper, 1953, 139 pp.

13. Examples of such surveys that have been published are:
New York's Senior Citizens, Our Most Neglected Resource; Our Most Important Challenge, Our Greatest Opportunity. New York City, Mayor's Advisory Committee for the Aged, Vols. I, II, III, 1949, 1949, 1953, 26 pp., 65 pp., 109 pp.
Widening the Lengthened Path of Life. Baltimore City, Commission on Aging and the Problems of the Aged, 1955, 89 pp.
The Senior Citizen in Our Community. Long Beach, Calif., Community Welfare Council, 1955, 59 pp.
Mauser, F. F., and J. H. Brown. *Detroit's Senior Citizens; Their Viewpoints and Attitudes.* Detroit, Wayne University, 1955, 53 pp.

14. Breckinridge, E. (project director). *Community Services for Older People: The Chicago Plan.* Chicago, Wilcox & Follett, 1952, 240 pp.

15. Kutner, B., D. Fanshel, and T. S. Langner. *Five Hundred Over Sixty.* New York, Cornell University Medical College, 1954, 316 pp.

16. A national directory of facilities for the aging was published in 1956 by F. A. Riley & Company of San Antonio, Texas.

17. Watkins, E. G. *Friendly Visitors.* Chicago, American Public Welfare Association, 1955, 15 pp.
Perkins, V. *Friendly Visiting.* Dallas, Texas, E. D. Farmer Foundation for the Aged, January 1954, Bull. No. 3, 3 pp.

Chapter 9

1. Shock, N. W. *A Classified Bibliography of Gerontology and Geriatrics.* Stanford, Calif., Stanford University Press, 1951, 599 pp.

2. Shock, N. W. *A Classified Bibliography of Gerontology and Geriatrics: Supplement One, 1949–1955.* Stanford, Calif., Stanford University Press, 1957, 526 pp.

3. Stieglitz, E. J. *Report of a Survey of Active Studies on Gerontology.* Unit on Gerontology, NIH, USPHS, 1942, 62 pp.

4. Editorial, "Can Research on Aging Flourish?" *J. Geront.,* 3: 141–42, 1948.

5. Shock, N. W. *Trends in Gerontology.* Stanford, Calif., Stanford University Press, 1951, 153 pp.

6. Deignan, S. L. and E. Miller. "The Support of Research in the Biosciences for the Fiscal Years 1952 and 1953," *Science,* 119: 661–67, 1954.

7. Birren, J. E. "Appendix A—Current Research on Aging," in J. E. Anderson (ed.), *Psychological Aspects of Aging.* Washington, D.C., American Psychological Association, 1956, pp. 290–92.

8. *Journal of Gerontology,* 9: 74, 1954.

9. These figures do not include intramural funds allocated by the National Institutes of Health for support of the Section on Gerontology of the National Heart Institute or of the Section on Aging of the National Institute of Mental Health.

10. Cowdry, E. V. (ed.). *Problems of Ageing.* 1st ed. Baltimore, Williams & Wilkins Co., 1939, 758 pp.

11. In this section, only references to books and review articles are given. References to specific research reports will be found in the complete bibliographies (References 1 and 2 of this chapter) and in the "Index to Current Periodical Literature" published in the *Journal of Gerontology.*

12. Cowdry, E. V. (ed.). *Problems of Ageing.* 2d ed. Baltimore, Williams & Wilkins Co., 1942, 936 pp.
   Lansing, A. I. (ed.). *Cowdry's Problems of Ageing.* 3d ed. Baltimore, Williams & Wilkins Co., 1952, 1061 pp.

13. Gardner, T. S. "An Evaluative Comparison of the Three Editions of *Cowdry's Problems of Ageing,*" *J. Geront.,* 8: 349–54, 1953.

14. Comfort, A. *The Biology of Senescence.* New York, Rinehart, 1956, 257 pp.

15. Moore, J. E., H. H. Merritt, and R. J. Masselink (eds.). *The Neurologic and Psychiatric Aspects of the Disorders of Ageing.* Vol. 35 of *Res. Publ. Ass. nerv. ment. Dis.,* 1956, 307 pp.

16. Summarized by M. B. Rockstein in W. S. Spector (ed.), *Handbook of Biological Data.* Philadelphia, Saunders, 1956, Table 152, pp. 182–86.

17. Andrew, W. *Cellular Changes with Age.* Springfield, Ill., Charles C Thomas, 1952, 74 pp.

18. Shock, N. W. "Age Changes in Some Physiologic Processes," *Geriatrics,* 12 : 40–48, 1957.
19. Engle, E. T., and G. Pincus (eds.). *Hormones and the Aging Process.* New York, Academic Press, 1956, 323 pp.
20. *Symposium on Problems of Gerontology.* National Vitamin Foundation, 15 East 58th Street, New York, 1954, No. 9, 141 pp.
21. Stieglitz, E. J. (ed.). *Geriatric Medicine.* 3d ed. Philadelphia, Lippincott, 1954, 718 pp.
     Thewlis, M. W. *The Care of the Aged (Geriatrics).* 6th ed. St. Louis, Mosby, 1954, 832 pp.
     Boas, E. P. *Treatment of the Patients Past Fifty.* 3d ed. Chicago, Year Book Publishers, 1947, 479 pp.
22. Monroe, R. T. *Diseases in Old Age.* Cambridge, Harvard University Press, 1951, 407 pp.
23. Shock, N. W. "Gerontology (Later Maturity)," in C. P. Stone and D. W. Taylor (eds.), *Ann. Rev. Psych.,* 1951, pp. 353–70.
     Kaplan, O. J. (ed.). *Mental Disorders in Later Life.* 2d ed. Stanford, Calif., Stanford University Press, 1956, 508 pp.
     Lorge, I. "Gerontology (Later Maturity)," in P. R. Farnsworth and Q. McNemar (eds.), *Ann. Rev. Psych.,* 1956, pp. 349–64.
     Gilbert, J. G. *Understanding Old Age.* New York, Ronald Press, 1952, 422 pp.
     Anderson, J. E. (ed.). *Psychological Aspects of Aging.* Washington, D.C., American Psychological Association, 1956, 323 pp.
24. Welford, A. T. *Skill and Age.* London, Nuffield Foundation, Oxford University Press, 1950, 161 pp.
25. Lehman, H. C. *Age and Achievement.* Princeton, N.J., Princeton University Press, 1953, 359 pp.
26. Cavan, R. S., E. W. Burgess, R. J. Havighurst, and H. Goldhamer. *Personal Adjustment in Old Age.* Chicago, Science Research Associates, Inc., 1949, 204 pp.
27. Havighurst, R. J., and R. Albrecht. *Older People.* New York, Longmans, Green, 1953, 415 pp.
28. Friedmann, E. A., and R. J. Havighurst. *The Meaning of Work and Retirement.* Chicago, University of Chicago Press, 1954, 197 pp.
29. Kutner, B., D. Fanshel, A. M. Togo, and T. S. Langner. *Five Hundred Over Sixty.* New York, Russell Sage Foundation, 1956, 345 pp.
     Corson, J. J., and J. W. McConnell. *Economic Needs of Older People.* New York, Twentieth Century Fund, 1956, 533 pp.

Chapter 10

1. This committee includes the following: E. V. Cowdry (Cancer Research), Marion Bunch (Psychology), E. F. Gildea (Neuropsychi-

atry), Helen Hayden (Social Work), E. H. Hopkins (Vice-Chancellor for University Development), J. E. Kirk (Gerontology), W. B. Kountz (Geriatrics), A. S. Queen (Sociology), W. H. Reals (Adult Education), and R. M. Trump (Business and Public Administration).

2. For list of the proceedings of these conferences, see Reference 18, Chapter 7.

3. For list of the proceedings of these conferences, see Reference 16, Chapter 7.

4. Cavan, R. S., E. W. Burgess, R. J. Havighurst, and H. Goldhamer. *Personal Adjustment in Old Age.* Chicago, Science Research Associates, Inc., 1949, 204 pp.

5. Havighurst, R. J., and R. Albrecht. *Older People.* New York, Longmans, Green, 1953, 415 pp.

6. Friedmann, E. A., and R. J. Havighurst. *The Meaning of Work and Retirement.* Chicago, University of Chicago Press, 1954, 197 pp.

7. Havighurst, R. J. "Personal and Social Adjustment," in J. E. Anderson (ed.), *Psychological Aspects of Aging.* Washington, D.C., American Psychological Association, 1956, pp. 54–71.

8. Binet, L., and F. Bourlière. *Précis de Gerontologie.* Paris, Masson et Cie, 1955, 554 pp.

9. Eckerström, S., and T. Geill. *Geriatri.* Copenhagen, Rosenkilde og Bagger, 1955, 216 pp.

10. Bürger, M. *Altern und Krankheit.* Leipzig, Veb Georg Thieme, 1954, 600 pp.

11. Baguena, M. Beltran. *Lecciones de Geriatria. Enfermedades de la Vejez.* Valencia, Editorial Saber. Vols. I and II, 1947, 131 pp. and 267 pp.; Vol. III, 1948, 538 pp.

INDEX